Folens

Essential Scripts and Screenplays

Models for Writing

Elizabeth Clark

Editor: Alison MacTier
Layout: 2i Design, Cambridge
Cover design: 2i Design, Cambridge

First published 2002 by Folens Limited.

Every effort has been made to trace the copyright holders of material used in this publication. If any copyright holder has been overlooked, we should be pleased to make any necessary arrangements.

British Library Cataloguing in Publication Data. A catalogue record for this publication is available from the British Library.

ISBN 1 84303 232 5

Acknowledgements

Text extracts: Approximately 850 words (pp 446–448, 451–452) from *Blackadder Goes Forth* in *Blackadder: The Whole Damn Dynasty* (Michael Joseph, 1988), copyright © Richard Curtis and Ben Elton, 1989; *Bram Stoker's Dracula* by James V Hart, published by Newmarket Press, © Columbia Pictures 1992; *Nosferatu* 1922; *The Hunchback of Notre Dame*, animated film by Walt Disney based on the novel *Notre-Dame de Paris* by Victor Hugo; *The Crucible* by Arthur Miller, published by Heinemann Educational Books Ltd copyright © 1952, 1953 by Arthur Miller; 'Smashie and Nicey' from *Harry Enfield and Chums*, produced by Tiger Aspect; 'Competitive Dad' from *The Fast Show*, produced by the BBC; *Knight Rider* by Glen A Larson, contributing writer R A Cinader/produced by Universal MCA; Extract from *The Adventure of the Illustrious Client* by Denis Green and Bruce Taylor based on a story by Arthur Conan Doyle; *A Streetcar Named Desire* by Tennessee Williams Copyright © 1947, 1953 renewed 1975, 1981 The University of the South, Published by New Directions, Reprinted by permission of the The University of the South, Sewanee, Tennessee. All rights whatsoever in this play are strictly reserved and application for performance etc., must be made before rehearsal to Casarotto Ramsay & Associates Ltd., National House, 60–66 Wardour Street, London W1V 4ND. No performance may be given unless a licence has been obtained; *Only Fools and Horses* by John Sullivan, published by BBC Worldwide Limited © John Sullivan 1999; *William Shakespeare's Romeo and Juliet*, adapted for the screen by Craig Pearce and Baz Luhrmann, produced by Twentieth Century Fox; *The Sixth Sense*, by M Night Shyamalan, produced by Buena Vista International; *Mary Shelley's Frankenstein*, adapted from the novel by Mary Shelley, by Steph Lady and Frank Darabont, published by Newmarket Press, © 1994 Tristar Pictures, *Zero Hour*, adapted by Anthony Ellis from the story by Ray Bradbury; *The Granny Project*, a stage play based on her own novel by Anne Fine, published by Collins Educational; *Absolutely Fabulous* by Jennifer Saunders, published by the Penguin Group and BBC Worldwide Ltd, copyright © Mr & Mrs Monsoon Ltd, 1994; Extract from *EastEnders* by Tony Jordan; *Shakespeare in Love*, screenplay by Marc Norman and Tom Stoppard, published by Faber and Faber.

Photographs: Cover Image, *Romeo and Juliet*: by Elliott Franks/PAL; pages 7–10 *Blackadder*: BBC Picture Archives; pages 24–25 *The Crucible*: © Donald Cooper/Photostage; page 27 Scene from *Sparkleshark*: © Donald Cooper/Photostage; pages 28–29 'Smashie and Nicey': BBC Picture Archives; page 32 *The Fast Show*: BBC Picture Archives with thanks to Simon Day; pages 36, 38, 39 Casino shot: Getty Images/Stone; page 41 David Hasselhoff: Rob Howard/Famous; pages 43, 50 *A Streetcar Named Desire*: © Donald Cooper/Photostage; pages 52–53, 56 *Only Fools and Horses*: BBC Picture Archives; page 57 *The Lion King*: Catherine Ashmore © Disney; pages 58, 62–63 *Romeo and Juliet*: by Elliott Franks/PAL; page 70 *The Sixth Sense*: Image supplied by The BFI; page 77 Sci-fi image: © Corbis; page 78 © Corel; pages 80, 87 Open door: © Corbis; page 91 *Twelfth Night*: © Donald Cooper/Photostage; pages 92–94, 97 *Absolutely Fabulous*: BBC Picture Archives; pages 98–99, 104 *EastEnders*: BBC Picture Archives; pages 98–103, 106–107 Background map of the Thames: reproduced by kind permission of the BBC; pages 108–109 *Twelfth Night*: © Donald Cooper/Photostage; pages 115–116 *Shakespeare in Love*: Image supplied by The BFI.

Illustrations: pages 64, 69: Jennifer Steele.

Contents

Contents

Essential Scripts and Screenplays

Your questions answered:

So this is a book all about plays, is it?

No, this is a book about different types of script – scripts for plays, films, radio and television. The best thing to do is to take a flick through it and see what catches your eye: after all, there are 21 scripts and screenplays in total, each chosen carefully.

So, what's so essential about it?

The texts have been carefully chosen to present the best examples of script writing around – and to show you how professional writers do it. With this book, your own writing will be better.

Why does it have that other title – 'Models for Writing'?

Well, although you will read each text first, the point of the book is to help you learn about key features good writers use in order to get their message across, or to entertain the reader. In other words, provide you with models that you can imitate. Scriptwriting is much more than just writing names on the left-hand side of the page and getting rid of speech marks.

How does it help me? I don't know what these key features are.

The book is divided into seven sections. Each section focuses on a specific aspect of script writing, such as how to develop characters or look through the eye of the director. In addition, the grouping of texts will help you make comparisons and contrasts between them, and see how, for example, different writers deal with the same story.

Also, every single text is preceded by a section called 'About the text'. This asks you to look out for key things, at Word, Sentence and Whole Text level, as you read. In this way, the key features will be clear to you. In addition, the very first section, 'That's entertainment', shows you a wide variety of script types to bring out the major differences between them, before you start.

Sounds good, but why should I take this seriously?

The writer is Elizabeth Clark, an experienced English teacher and writer. She is very well placed to give you advice, and provide you with interesting and wide-ranging examples of scripts that she has found exciting and stimulating. She has even persuaded the *EastEnders* producer to let her use a script from a particularly dramatic episode (see Chapter 6).

Ultimately, however, you should read the texts to enjoy them, and through reading and studying them you will improve your writing skills. This will be of benefit to all your school work, and will prepare you for examinations and other forms of assessment. Most of all, the book will make you more like a real writer, in the real world.

That's entertainment!

About the chapter

This chapter contains a range of scripts and screenplays that introduce you to some of the main features and skills related to this form of writing. You will notice, as you read them, that they do not always have consistent layout, some contain more dialogue than others and some provide more information about the setting than others.

introducing scripts and screenplays

About the text

The first script in this chapter comes from the popular TV series *Blackadder*. There were four series broadcast, each dealing with a different period in history, but all featuring Edmund Blackadder and Baldrick (in different roles). There are two extracts here, both from the final episode of the last series *Blackadder Goes Forth*, which is set in the trenches during the First World War.

As you read these extracts, consider the following features of the text:

Word level:

- Which words and phrases firmly establish the time in which this extract is set?

Sentence level:

- What differences do you notice in the tone of the language used by Baldrick and that used by Blackadder?

- How are questions used for varying effects within the extracts?

Text level:

- What impressions are built up about each of the characters as you read both extracts?

- How do the stage directions and information about setting in the second extract build up a sense of tension and then develop beyond this?

Previous page: Blackadder, played by Rowan Atkinson, in the third series, *Blackadder the Third*.

This page: Baldrick, played by Tony Robinson, in conversation with Blackadder, played by Rowan Atkinson.

Blackadder

Extract 1

BALDRICK

I thought it was going to be such fun too. We all did. Joining a local regiment and everything. The Turnip Street Workhouse Pals: I'll never forget. It was great – the first time I ever felt popular, everyone was cheering and throwing flowers, a girl actually came up and kissed me.

BLACKADDER

[*To GEORGE*] Poor woman – first casualty of the war.

BALDRICK

I loved the training, all we had to do was bayonet sacks full of straw – even I could do it. I remember telling my mum, "these sacks will be easy to outwit in a battle situation".

BLACKADDER throws BALDRICK a look and bangs his pipe on the post.

And then we all met up just before Christmas 1914… .

GEORGE

Yes, that's right. I'd just arrived and we had that wonderful Christmas truce … do you remember, sir? We could hear 'Silent Night' drifting across the still clear air of No Man's Land… . And then they came, the Germans … emerging out of the freezing night mist, calling to us, and we clambered up over the top and went to meet them… .

BLACKADDER

Both sides advanced further during one Christmas piss-up than we've managed in the next two and a half years.

BALDRICK

Sir, sir, do you remember the football match, sir?

BLACKADDER

Remember it? How could I forget it. I was *never* offside, I could not *believe* that decision!

BALDRICK

Since then we've been stuck here for three flipping years, we haven't moved! All my friends are dead: my pet spider, Sammy, Katie the worm, Bertie the bird – everyone except Neville the fat hamster.

BLACKADDER

[*Solemn*] I'm afraid Neville bought it too, Baldrick … I'm sorry.

BALDRICK

Neville – gone, sir?

BLACKADDER

Actually, not quite gone, he's in the corner bunging up the sink.

BALDRICK gets up and wanders across the room.

BALDRICK

[*Upset*] But it didn't have to happen. If it wasn't for this terrible war Neville might still be alive today, sniffling his little nose and going "eek".

BLACKADDER

On the other hand, if he hadn't died I wouldn't have been able to insert a curtain rod in his bottom and use him as a dishmop.

BALDRICK

Why can't we just stop, sir? Why can't we just say, "no more killing, let's all go home"? Why can't we pack it in? Why?

GEORGE

[*Leaping up*] Now, look here, you just stop that conchie talk right now, Private. It's absurd, it's bolshevism and wouldn't work anyway.

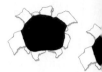

BALDRICK

[*Innocently*] But why not, sir?

GEORGE

Why not? Erm, you mean, why, why wouldn't it work? Well, it wouldn't work, because … it wouldn't work because … get on with polishing your boots, Private – and less of that lip.

He turns to BLACKADDER.

It's all right, sir – I think I've managed to crush the mutiny. To think, in a few hours, at last we're going to be off! Not that I won't miss all this though – ha – we've had some times, haven't we? We've had damnably good laughs, eh?

Pause.

BLACKADDER

Yes. Can't think of any specific ones myself.

George, played by Hugh Laurie.

Extract 2

Outside is heard the muffled faraway cry:
"Stand to, stand to, fix bayonets!"

BLACKADDER
Come on, come on, let's move.

They all move out. At the door, BLACKADDER turns to GEORGE.

Don't forget your stick, Lieutenant.

GEORGE
[*Picking up his stick*] Rather, sir. We wouldn't want to face a machine-gun without this.

They emerge in the misty trenches and all stand in a line, ready for the off.
Then suddenly there is a silence. The machine-guns stop.

DARLING
I say, Listen – our guns have stopped.

GEORGE
You don't think … .

BALDRICK
Perhaps the war's over. Perhaps it's peace.

GEORGE
Hurrah! The big nobs have got round a table and yanked the iron out of the fire.

DARLING
Thank God – we lived through it – The Great War, 1914 to 1917.

ALL THREE
Hip hip hurray!!!

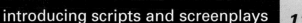

BLACKADDER
I'm afraid not. The guns have stopped because we are about to attack. Not even our generals are mad enough to shell their own men. They feel it's more sporting to let the Germans do it.

GEORGE
So, we are, in fact, going over. This is, as they say, it?

BLACKADDER
Yes, unless I think of something very quickly.

A command is heard: "Company, one pace forward." They all take one step forward.

BALDRICK
There's a nasty splinter on that ladder, sir. A bloke could hurt himself on that.

A call: "Stand ready." They put their hands on the ladders, ready to climb over.

I have a plan, sir.

BLACKADDER
Really, Baldrick, a cunning and subtle one?

BALDRICK
Yes, sir.

BLACKADDER
As cunning as a fox who's just been appointed Professor of Cunning at Oxford University?

BALDRICK
Yes, sir.

Another call is heard: "On the signal, Company will advance."

BLACKADDER
Well, I'm afraid it's too late. Whatever it was, I'm sure it was better than my plan to get out of this by pretending to be mad. I mean, who would have noticed another madman round here?

A whistle goes. He looks at BALDRICK.

Good luck, everyone.

BLACKADDER blows his whistle. There is a roar of voices – everyone leaps up the ladders. As they rise above the sandbags they are met by thunderous machine-gun fire.

BLACKADDER, BALDRICK, GEORGE and DARLING run on, brandishing their hand-guns. They will not get far.

Silence falls. Our soldiers fade away. No Man's Land turns slowly into a peaceful field of poppies. The only sound is that of a bird, singing sweetly.

About the text

The two script extracts provided here deal with the same character – Dracula, or Nosferatu as he is also known. The first is taken from the 1992 film *Bram Stoker's Dracula*, written by James V Hart, which starred Gary Oldman in the title role and was directed by Francis Ford Coppola. In it, the original American spelling has been retained. The second comes from the earlier silent film *Nosferatu* made in 1922. The dialogue shown here was displayed on the screen for the audience to read. Both extracts show the dramatic ending of the films.

As you read these extracts, consider the following features of the texts:

Word level:

- How do the screenwriters create a sense of pace through the choice of language used in both scenes?

Sentence level:

- What differences do you notice between the sentences in the stage directions of both extracts?

- Why do you think there are these differences?

Text level:

- How are the themes of good and evil developed within both extracts?

- What different views of Dracula or Nosferatu are conveyed?

Bram Stoker's Dracula

MINA and DRACULA

DRACULA turns to her. His face horribly transformed.

DRACULA
[*tender, loving*]
Mina ...?

She holds his dying gaze. He turns and drags himself toward the chapel. MINA backs slowly after him, her gun on the men.

MINA
When my time comes – will you do the same to me? *Will you?*

On men over MINA

HOLMWOOD looking at her, the rifle pointing at him. HARKER, loving her, begins to understand.

HOLMWOOD tries to rush to her. HARKER holds him back, understanding MINA's resolve.

HARKER
No, let them go. Let her go. Our work is finished here ... hers is just begun.

Closeup VAN HELSING nods knowingly. HARKER has learned from his nightmare.

Closeup MINA

She aims pointblank at HARKER.

On HARKER over MINA

She fires! We pull back to see a wolf leaping from the ramparts at him, crashing to the ground – dead.

Back to MINA and DRACULA

MINA backs after DRACULA into the castle, never taking

her eyes or her gun off the men.

Chapel door – sunset

Medium wide shot

HARKER waits at the chapel door nervously. HOLMWOOD is pacing, pounding his fists futilely against it. VAN HELSING holds his hand up, indicating that they should be still.

SEWARD cradles QUINCEY

He dies ... .

On VAN HELSING

He drops his gun and faces the chapel. He bows his head, praying intensely.

VAN HELSING
Rest him. Let him sleep in peace... . We have become God's mad men.

Castle chapel – sunset

Wide shot

DRACULA and MINA on the altar steps. Deep in the caverns of his eyes, fierce life still burns. We track in on them.

DRACULA
Where is my God? He forsakes me.

MINA grips the handle of the knife and tries to pull it out. His fingers, nearly bone, creep up the shaft, stopping her.

DRACULA
It is finished.

Filled with love, she stares down into his eyes. She cradles him, kissing him, smoothing his matted, graying hair. Suddenly she speaks intimately in Roumanian – he responds.

MINA
No ... my love –

He shudders, blood welling up from the wound in his heart.

DRACULA
Give me peace.

View on the steps – high overhead angle

Old candles light themselves. The shadow of the crucifix moves across the floor as MINA, glowing, moves into the place and manner as when ELIZABETH lay there.

DRACULA raises his eyes to ... ELIZABETH.

Camera starts slowly booming down.

She rises up and kisses him. Camera moves closer. His youth is restored. She comforts him. He puts her hand on the knife in his heart. MINA's hands on the knife. She quakes, knowing what she must do. She closes her eyes, prays for strength, and falls on him with all her weight, driving the knife clear through his heart.

Close shot – the knife

The steel point penetrating the ground.

NOSFERATU

NINA had promised her husband never to open The Book of the Vampires, but she found herself unable to resist the temptation.

In the living room of the HARKERS, NINA reads from The Book of the Vampires.

One can recognize the mark of the vampire by the trace of his fangs on the victim's throat. Only a woman can break his frightful spell – a woman pure in heart – who will offer her blood freely to NOSFERATU and will keep the vampire by her side until after the cock has crowed.

Enter HARKER

NINA
[*pointing out the window to the mansion across the street*]
Look! Every night, in front of me!

The townspeople lived in mortal terror. Who was sick or dying? Who will be stricken tomorrow?

At the HARKERS' House NINA lies sick in bed.

HARKER
Don't be frightened. I will get the professor.

Exit HARKER.

NINA looks out the window at the line of coffins being carried along the street. She reads from The Book of the Vampires.

Only a woman can break his frightful spell – a woman pure in heart – who will offer her blood freely to NOSFERATU and will keep the vampire by her side until after the cock has crowed.

MEANWHILE Outside the sanatarium. Two old women talk to each other.

OLD WOMAN
They saw him escape. He strangled his keeper.

RENFIELD runs down an alley, pursued by a crowd. He climbs onto a roof. The crowd throws rocks at him. He climbs down and runs outside of town. The crowd pursues.

THAT NIGHT. In the HARKERS' Bedroom. NINA is awakened by the NOSFERATU outside her window. She opens the window.

HARKER awakens and NINA faints in his arms.

HARKER
The professor! Call the professor!

Exit HARKER.

Enter the NOSFERATU.

THE NEXT MORNING

In the HARKERS' Bedroom. The cock crows. The NOSFERATU looks up from drinking at NINA'S neck.

MEANWHILE In RENFIELD'S Cell at the Sanatorium.

RENFIELD
Master! Master! Beware!

*Outside the HARKERS' House. HARKER and
VAN HELSING arrive.*

*In the HARKERS' Bedroom. Sunlight sweeps across the
buildings across the street from NINA'S window.*

*NOSFERATU attempts to escape but is touched by the
sunlight.*

He vanishes in a puff of smoke.

In RENFIELD'S Cell at the Sanatorium.

RENFIELD
The Master is dead.

In the HARKERS' Bedroom NINA awakens.

Enter HARKER

NINA
Jonathon!

HARKER takes NINA in his arms as she dies.

And at that moment, as if by a miracle, the sick no
longer died, and the stifling shadow of the vampire
vanished with the morning sun.

THE END

About the text

The story of the Hunchback of Notre Dame comes from Victor Hugo's epic novel *Notre-Dame de Paris*. It has been filmed before, but the extract here is taken from Walt Disney's animated version. Quasimodo is the hunchback who rings the bells in Paris' mighty church. This is from the final section of the film.

As you read this extract, consider the following features of the text:

Word level:

- How does the language of Frollo firmly establish him as the villain in this extract? Consider specific words he uses, or the way he speaks specific words.

Sentence level:

- How does the final 'staging information' passage connect ideas together to develop a sense of pace and urgency?

Text level:

- What images can you find in this extract that highlight the theme of good versus evil?

Meanwhile, VICTOR is using HUGO as a bellows to warm up the fire on the lead pot. QUASI attaches a rope to it, then dumps it over, sending fire pouring out of the tower and on to the scattering guards below. The guards battering the door run, but FROLLO manages to get inside the cathedral safely. As he does, the ARCHDEACON runs up to him.

ARCHDEACON
Frollo, have you gone mad? I will not tolerate this assault on the house of God!

He shoves the ARCHDEACON to the ground.

FROLLO
Silence, you old fool! The hunchback and I have unfinished business to attend to. And this time, you will not interfere.

He closes the door and locks it from the inside. Upstairs, QUASI bursts into the bedroom jubilantly.

QUASIMODO
We've done it, Esmeralda! We've beaten them back! Come and see!

She doesn't move.

QUASIMODO
Esmeralda? Wake up! You're safe now.

He pauses, but still nothing.

QUASIMODO
Esmeralda? Oh, no!

He gets a spoonful of water, and tries to make her drink it. She doesn't.

QUASIMODO
Oh no.

He begins to cry. FROLLO enters and touches QUASI on his hump.

QUASIMODO
You killed her.

FROLLO
It was my duty, horrible as it was. I hope you can forgive me. There, there, Quasimodo, I know it hurts. But now, the time has come to end your suffering.

We see that FROLLO has a dagger. As FROLLO raises it to stab him, QUASI sees the shadow of the dagger. He turns and struggles with FROLLO only briefly, before wresting the dagger from FROLLO'S hands and backing him into a corner.

FROLLO
Now, now, listen to me,
Quasimodo.

QUASIMODO
No, you listen! All my life you
have told me the world is a dark,
cruel place. But now, I see that the
only thing dark and cruel about it
is people like you!

He throws away the dagger.

ESMERALDA
Quasimodo?

*He turns and sees ESMERALDA
sitting on the bed.*

QUASIMODO
Esmeralda!

FROLLO
She lives!

FROLLO grabs a sword.

QUASIMODO
No!

*He grabs ESMERALDA and runs
out on to the balcony. FROLLO
follows, but when he gets outside, he
sees nothing but gargoyles [including
a Pumbaa 'goyle]. After looking left
and right, he looks out over the edge*

*and finds QUASI hanging there
with ESMERALDA.*

FROLLO
Leaving so soon?

*He swings his sword, but QUASI
dodges the blow by swinging to
another spot. Down on the ground,
the guards stop to watch.*

GUARD
Up there!

FROLLO goes to swing again.

QUASIMODO
Hang on!

*QUASI swings off again, just
narrowly missing FROLLO'S
sword. Finally, FROLLO gets
QUASI cornered.*

FROLLO
I should have known you'd risk
your life to save that gypsy witch.
Just as your own mother died
trying to save you.

QUASIMODO
What!?!

FROLLO
Now I'm going to do what I should
have done twenty years ago!

He swings his cape, covering QUASI'S head. But as he tries to throw QUASI off the balcony, the panicking QUASI pulls FROLLO off as well. Now FROLLO is hanging onto QUASI, who is hanging onto ESMERALDA. FROLLO throws his cape around another gargoyle, and pulls himself over. He stands up and is about to swing at ESMERALDA.

FROLLO
And He shall smite the wicked and plunge them into the fiery pit!

The gargoyle, however, begins to crack. FROLLO is thrown off balance, and hangs onto the gargoyle's head. Suddenly, the 'goyle comes to life and roars. FROLLO screams, and the now stone gargoyle breaks off, sending FROLLO falling to his death. Meanwhile, ESMERALDA is losing her grip on QUASIMODO.

ESMERALDA
Quasimodo! Quasi!

He slips loose and begins to fall.

ESMERALDA
No!!!

He falls right along the building, close enough for PHOEBUS to catch him several floors below and pull him back into the building. When QUASI sees who has caught him, he and PHOEBUS hug. ESMERALDA comes running in. After ESMERALDA hugs him, he takes ESMERALDA'S hand and PHOEBUS' hand, and puts them together. They kiss, and QUASI smiles broadly. Cut to ground level, where PHOEBUS and ESMERALDA emerge into the light. As the crowd cheers, ESMERALDA turns back to the open doorway. She comes back and leads out QUASIMODO. The crowd goes silent. Soon, a little girl cautiously comes forward from the crowd. She looks at him, then pets his face. They then hug, and QUASI picks her up and put her up on his shoulder. The crowd begins to cheer. As he moves into the crowd, they do not move away as before. The 'goyles are above, breaking out the champagne.

CLOPIN
Three cheers for Quasimodo!!

The crowd breaks into loud cheering.

About the text

The Crucible, a play by Arthur Miller, is set in Salem, Massachusetts – home to the famous witchcraft trials in 1692. Salem was an extremely religious community and, in his play, Miller shows how the community was torn apart by accusations of 'dealing with the devil'.

In this short extract, we see John Proctor, a once proud man who has been tortured in jail, being allowed to see his pregnant wife, Elizabeth, before he is sent to his death at the gallows. Until now, he has refused to compromise his principles and sign a declaration to say he has done wrong, but the meeting has been set up in the hope that his wife will be able to change his mind.

As you read this extract, consider the following features of the text:

Word level:

- Which aspects of the language used by the characters convey a sense of time to the reader or audience?

Sentence level:

- How is the atmosphere of this final scene created, in part, by effective use of verbs within the stage directions?

Text level:

- How do our feelings towards the characters develop as this scene unfolds?

- How does the writer avoid this scene becoming over sentimental? (Is there any mention of always loving him/her?) Compare the ordinary nature of what is actually said between them, with the description surrounding it.

The Crucible

Act 4

A sound – the sibilance of dragging feet on stone. They turn. A pause.

HERRICK enters with JOHN PROCTOR. His wrists are chained. He is another man, bearded, filthy, his eyes misty as though webs had overgrown them. He halts inside the doorway, his eye caught by the sight of ELIZABETH. The emotion flowing between them prevents anyone from speaking for an instant. Now HALE, visibly affected, goes to DANFORTH and speaks quietly.

HALE
Pray, leave them, Excellency.

DANFORTH
(*pressing HALE impatiently aside*)
Mr Proctor, you have been notified, have you not? (*PROCTOR is silent, staring at ELIZABETH.*) I see light in the sky, Mister; let you counsel with your wife, and may God help you turn your back on Hell. (*PROCTOR is silent, staring at ELIZABETH.*)

HALE
(*quietly*) Excellency, let–

DANFORTH brushes past HALE and walks out. HALE follows. CHEEVER stands and follows, HATHORNE behind. HERRICK goes. PARRIS, from a safe distance, offers:

A scene showing John and Elizabeth Proctor from a stage production of *The Crucible*.

PARRIS
If you desire a cup of cider, Mr Proctor, I am sure I– (*PROCTOR turns an icy stare at him, and he breaks off. PARRIS raises his palms towards PROCTOR.*) God lead you now. (*PARRIS goes out.*)

Alone, PROCTOR walks to her, halts. It is as though they stood in a spinning world. It is beyond sorrow, above it. He reaches out his hand as though toward an embodiment not quite real, and as he touches her, a strange soft sound, half laughter, half amazement, comes from his throat. He pats her hand. She covers his hand with hers. And then, weak, he sits. Then she sits, facing him.

PROCTOR
The child?

ELIZABETH
It grows.

PROCTOR
There is no word of the boys?

ELIZABETH
They're well. Rebecca's Samuel keeps them.

PROCTOR
You have not seen them?

ELIZABETH
I have not. (*She catches a weakening in herself and downs it.*)

PROCTOR
You are a – marvel Elizabeth.

ELIZABETH
You – have been tortured?

PROCTOR
Aye. (*Pause. She will not let herself be drowned in the sea that threatens her.*) They come for my life now.

ELIZABETH
I know it.

②

Plays and players

About the chapter

This chapter contains three extracts from television programmes, one is an American drama, *Knight Rider*, which was very popular in the early 1980s, the other two are comedy sketch shows made in the UK. The focus here is on the ways in which character is conveyed through the language used. In each case, the success of the programme is dependent on the creation of a very strong character, although for different reasons.

introducing character

About the text

Smashie and Nicey (from *Harry Enfield and Chums* – Smashie and Nicey) are two radio DJs, approaching middle-age, who are presented as being rather too full of themselves and superficial, as well as being out of touch with modern fashions and music. Every sketch ends with them playing the same old rock song – Bachman-Turner Overdrive's 'You ain't seen nothin' yet'. In this extract, the two DJs are discussing their holiday reading. They move on to the merits of Shakespeare, although, as you will see, the level of discussion is rather basic. You might also want to look out for the references to the 'charidy' work they do, which they say they don't like to talk about.

As you read this extract, consider the following features of the text:

Word level:

- Which 'words' within the dialogue of the sketch help to establish the 'over the top' characteristics of both DJs?

Sentence level

- Are there any features of 'parody' you can find in this text? In other words, how does the script mimic and mock real-life DJ-speak? For example, look at the use of repetition of key phrases and words.

Text level:

- In what ways is the ending of this extract ironic, given the exaggerated praise of holidays, Shakespeare, and the love of sunbathing?

Previous page: a scene from the National Youth Theatre's production of *Sparkleshark*.

Harry Enfield (HE) as Dave Nice,
Paul Whitehouse (PW) as Mike Smash.

Smashie and Nicey

Int. radio studio. PW is speaking into the microphone as HE comes in.

F1
'R-r-r-radio FAB, Radio FAB, Radio FAB-FM!'

PW
Mmm! Tastemungous. I'm just havin' a nice cup o' tea here. I love tea, don't you? Especially a nice cup. In the words of the old song, 'I like a nice cup o' tea!' Er, makes you think, doesn't it? Well, it makes me think, anyway – and, er, talkin' of all things nice, here's me old mate, Dave Nice! Just back from his holidays in Greece, and lookin' poppadappadobulous.

HE
Rockinabbadobulous to you, mate!

PW
Look's like you got a chance to, er, soak up some rays there, Nicey. Did you do a lot of sunbathin', mate?

HE
Sunbathin' mornin' noon and night, mate! Er, took a young friend of mine with me, and every day it was togs off, oil on, and down on the beach for a spot of sunbathin'.

PW
I love sunbathin'. I know when I'm on holiday, I love to, er, sunbathe.

HE
Did a lot of sunbathin', mate. You can't beat it, can you? Lyin' out there in the sun, er, sunbathin'. But you know the great thing about holidays apart from ...

HE + PW
... the, er, sunbathin'!

HE
... you get a chance to catch up on all your reading. Did a lot of reading of books out there, mate. All for charidy, of course.

PW
Books are fantabulous – aren't they, mate? Er, they're – I dunno – they're sort of like films in, er, word form.

HE
You're not wrong there, mate. I read Oliver by, er, Charles Dickens, the book of the film – none of the songs in there – but a bookmungous read, nevertheless. Er, some of the words he used are quite phenomenal.

PW
I know what you mean. Those old fashioned pilchards, they really knew how to, er, write down, sort of, what they'd been, er, thinkin' about, earlier, er... .

HE
Wise words, mate. Actually ... just look at old Shakespeare. All those plays from just the one guy, nobody to help him and only an old feather to write with? Quite phenomenal.

PW
I dunno, and, er, what a brogmungously megatastic contribution to, er, English language culture-wise, what with all that 'thee-thou' type stuff.

HE
Thou art not wrong there, mate – er, but that's enough chat from us old culture vultures.

PW
Sure is, mate. I'm gonna pop off home now. Well, because, er, you know – that's where I live.

HE
See ya, Smashie!

PW remains seated, but leans back from the microphone

HE
What a great guy – old Smashie, there. Does a lot of, er, work for charidy – doesn't like to talk about it. Right now, we're gonna get down to a real classic; Messrs Bachman Turner Overdrive with their interpretation of a Shakespeare play, 'Thou ain't seen nothin' yet!' Let's rock!

HE pulls a large lever, and the music starts. Now off-air, PW asks …

PW
So, er, Nicey, er, forgot to ask you, er, did you do any sunbathin' while you were on holiday?

HE
Not really, mate – weather was bloody awful.

Both continue nodding their heads appreciatively to the music.

About the text

This extract is taken from the BBC comedy sketch show, *The Fast Show*. As with many others in the show, the extract takes aspects of human behaviour and exaggerates them in order to create comedy. Here, we are introduced to a 'competitive dad' at Christmas time. 'Competitive Dad', played by Simon Day, always wants to do things rather than let his sons learn, and here we see him trying to redecorate the family Christmas tree. The situation is given an added twist by the arrival of Competitive Dad's own father, played by Mark Williams. Arabella Weir plays the part of Competitive Dad's wife.

As you read this extract, consider the following features of the text:

Word level:

- Which words and phrases firmly establish Competitive Dad's views on Christmas in the past and present?

Sentence level:

- What differences do you notice in the tone of the language used by Competitive Dad and that used by the grandfather?

Text level:

- How do the stage directions further develop our understanding of Competitive Dad?

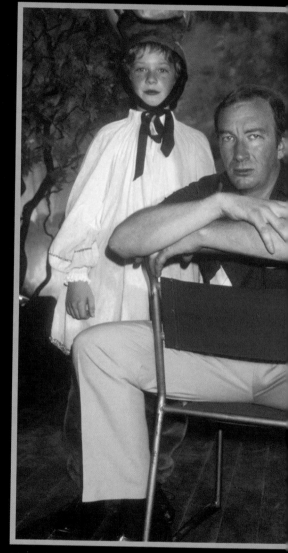

Simon Day, seated, who plays 'Competitive Dad' in the show.

Competitive Dad

int. living room – the two boys are decorating the Christmas tree.

B1
Can I put the fairy on top this year?

B2
Better let Dad – he might get upset.

Pause before SD comes in the room.

SD
No, no, no, no, no – you've got it completely wrong.

SD calls to AW, who's outside the room.

SD
Darling – come and see what these oafs have done to the tree.

AW comes in and comments.

AW
Good boys – it looks lovely.

which gets her a sour look from SD.

SD
I wish you'd back me up some times! It is Christmas after all.

AW glares at SD.

SD
All right – I'm sorry. It's just that we had such perfect Christmases when I was a boy. And those golden memories will live with me forever. I want Toby and Peter to have the same sort of memories.

Slight pause as SD looks at the tree again.

SD
We only had one rope of Christmas lights – not those ghastly coloured ones. [*to B1*] Take them down, Toby – they're an eyesore.

The front doorbell rings, as SD decides to add …

SD
And that tinsel.

Slight pause – AW goes to answer the door.

SD
Christmas Eve was my favourite. Mother and I would always decorate the tree. She always let me put the fairy on top.

AW appears at the door – shortly followed by an 'aged' MW.

AW
Darling, look who's here – it's your father.

MW
Hello, son!

*Slight pause as MW heartily shakes a cowed
SD's hand.*

SD
Hello, Dad. Off to Pat and Elma's?

MW
No – couldn't face it this year. Thought I'd come here.

MW spots the Christmas tree.

MW
Oh my giddy aunt – what have you done to that tree,
boy? Put some of those lovely coloured lights on,
there. You show him, Toby.

The boys start re-stringing the lights.

MW
Reminds me of those awful Christmases when you
were a boy. Your mother knew absolutely nothing
about decorating a tree! [*to B1*] That's it, Toby – put
some of that lovely tinsel on as well. [*to SD and AW*]
He knows what he's doing.

Pause as MW looks at SD expectantly.

MW
Aren't you going to offer me a drink?

SD
Yes, father.

A bent SD obediently scurries out of the room.

About the text

Two extracts from this feature-length TV film, based on the series *Knight Rider*, appear here. The first is set in a casino where detective Michael Long is on a surveillance operation. It is clearly building towards a moment of tension and drama although, from the extract, we do not know who will be the victors. The second extract shows Michael undergoing plastic surgery, having narrowly escaped death. It is clear that Michael's life will be changing course. In the series, the Knight 2000, mentioned in the second extract, turns out to be a talking, thinking car that can drive itself. In both extracts, the original American spelling has been retained.

As you read these extracts, consider the following features of the text:

Word level:

- In the first extract, how does the screenwriter use particular words within the stage directions to create a vivid picture of the different characters?

Sentence level:

- What do you notice about the tone of the language used by Knight in the second extract?

- What does this tell us about him?

Text level:

- How do the stage directions in Extract 1 differ from those in Extract 2, in terms of building the impressions of the characters?

- What differences would this make to an actor preparing for a role in either extract?

KNIGHT RIDER

Extract 1

Act One

FADE IN

RENO – NIGHT – ESTABLISHING – STOCK

EXT. ND HOTEL – NIGHT – STOCK

INT. CASINO – NIGHT – STOCK

Should be maximum up-key.

CLOSE ON CROUPIER TABLE [TO MATCH]

Action at the table, loud music from the lounge, CHARLES ACTON, fifty-five, graying temples, handsome and distinguished is on a roll. Quite appropriately standing next to him as if completing an ad for Gentleman's Quarterly, a woman wearing both furs and jewelry, none of which she'd need to be the centerpiece for the entire room. She is TANYA WALKER. She looks at her watch discreetly as CHARLES clenches his fist in conservative jubilance.

CROUPIER
Seven the winner.

A stack of hundred dollar checks is pushed at CHARLES and he modestly picks them up and places them in a chip holder already packed. He is having a very lucky night.

CLOSE ON	close-up
ESTABLISHING	opening shot, which sets the scene
EXT	exterior
FADE IN	gradually focus on a scene
INT	interior
ND	(neutral density) dim the shot
MAXIMUM UP-KEY	a lighting or camera instruction
STOCK	a non-specific shot

CHARLES

I can't seem to lose tonight.

TANYA

Don't say that. It could lead to bad luck.

CHARLES

I don't believe in luck.

As ACTON turns to look back at the game, TANYA'S eyes drift to WILSON, a husky man in a three-piece suit standing to the back of the gallery. He is chief of security for Consolidated Chemical Corporation, something we might deduce as we push in to a small earpiece with an inconspicuous, flesh-colored wire leading down into his suit. He lifts a hand to the earpiece, which brings his watch up into proximity to his mouth. When he speaks, it is surreptitiously unnoticed by people craning to see the game in front of him.

WILSON

OK, Lonnie. He's winning big. It's now or never.

WILSON turns his head and we follow his gaze to an elevator into which moves a statuesque dark-haired girl. Her name is LONNIE.

CLOSE ON LONNIE

PUSH IN camera lens zooms in

As the elevator doors close on her, we pull back to reveal the back of the head of a second man watching her progress. He too is wearing a telltale earpiece. He is standing farther back behind both WILSON and the game that is in progress. He is MICHAEL LONG. We see little of his face except to notice that he is young, has dark curly hair and rugged outlines to his sparsely seen features. He turns away from the game and we tilt down to avoid his face and see him flip a microswitch on his belt receiver/transmitter.

MICHAEL
I think it's coming down – Wilson just sent Lonnie into the elevator. Do you read?

A MAN STANDING ON A LADDER – MUNTZY wearing hotel coveralls.

MUNTZY
Loud and clear, Lieutenant. If she's coming – I'll have a front row seat.

He is changing a ceiling fixture as an elevator door opens down the corridor and LONNIE heads his way, giving him a smiling look as she moves past. He doesn't acknowledge the girl, continuing his work, obliviously.

LONNIE reaches a door, looks both ways.

POINT OF VIEW OF THE MAN ON THE LADDER.

No interest. She is relieved. She puts a key in the lock and enters … . We push back up to the man on the ladder, he turns his head to us, full on and we now see an earpiece.

Extract 2

A NEW ANGLE [SHOT]

on the strange death scene as suddenly something is happening as we perceive a strange whine far in the distance and camera tilts up to reveal a pinpoint of light far off on the horizon. The light grows larger and larger until it is directly overhead. Suddenly a powerful light bursts on, bathing the scene of carnage in dazzling brightness. Close on a weathered old face. The man is WILTON KNIGHT. He stares down from the hovering machine.

KNIGHT

My God. We're too late.

He signals and the machine begins to lower down to the highway.

SLOW DISSOLVE TO HIS POINT OF VIEW [SHOT]

where we see the body of MICHAEL sprawled in the dust.

THE KNIGHT ESTATE – DAY [SHOT]

as a twin turbine jet helicopter lands behind a massive house. On the machine is the logo of KNIGHT INDUSTRIES.

ON DOCTOR MILES [SHOT]

as he examines the now carefully bandaged and reconstructed form of MICHAEL LONG. He looks at a wall of medical instrumentation and examines the eyes of MICHAEL as WILTON KNIGHT enters the room.

KNIGHT

Well?

MILES

I'll give you the same answer I've given you the past four days. He's probably the only human being on this planet in worse condition than you.

KNIGHT

You have the bedside manner of a rattlesnake.

MILES

My deal with you was honesty.

KNIGHT

Is he going to die?

MILES

He should have. The bullet was fired into his head at point-blank range.

> **DISSOLVE** slowly fade from one shot to another

KNIGHT

Then how did he survive?

MILES

The man has a metal plate in his forehead. Military surgery, I'd suspect. It deflected the bullet away from a dead center hit in his brain and back out through his face. We'll never know what he looked like.

> ON MICHAEL
>
> *stirring restlessly … mumbling … crying out in anguish and anger.*
>
> *[Note: The following underlined dialogue will either be shot in closeup or v.o.]*

KNIGHT

<u>That's it, son … get mad … and stay mad. It will keep you living. Just like me.</u>

> *INT. THE ESTATE HOSPITAL ROOM [SHOT]*
>
> *DOCTOR MILES stands over MICHAEL who is prone on an operating table. KNIGHT looks on from across the room as, one by one, the delicate bandages come off.*
>
> *ON DEVON [SHOT]*
>
> *as he enters and moves up to KNIGHT.*

DEVON

I have good news for you. The KNIGHT 2000 will be ready by …

KNIGHT

Shhhh …

> *KNIGHT moves forward leaving DEVON mystified and not just mildly frustrated.*

DEVON

[*under breath*] I work these people around the clock and suddenly you aren't interested.

> *ON MILES [SHOT]*
>
> *as he masterfully lifts the final strip of adhesive and begins to unwrap MICHAEL'S face. KNIGHT moves in to stand beside him, and DEVON beside the two other men. We are looking up at them from MICHAEL'S point of view as they stare down, not revealing anything.*

David Hasselhoff, who starred in the title role of the TV series.

V.O.	voice over

ON MICHAEL KNIGHT [SHOT]

A new face, far more rugged than his former image. Character and age somehow replacing youthful naivety.

MICHAEL
That bad?

MILES
On the contrary. An excellent job if I do say so myself. Why don't you look for yourself?

Almost reluctantly, MICHAEL rises up and moves slowly across the room to a mirror.

KNIGHT
Perfection.

MICHAEL
It isn't me.

MICHAEL raises his fingers up to feel the unfamiliar contours.

DEVON
You now have a second chance to live. Unless you'd prefer to walk around with a face that could get you killed all over again?

MICHAEL turns a sober look towards KNIGHT.

KNIGHT
Take my word. You'll be much safer with this face. And it's rather handsome if I do say so myself.

DEVON leans in.

DEVON
Does it strike you that there's an uncanny resemblance between this fellow and you as a young man?

KNIGHT shoots DEVON a wilting glare.

DEVON
Just my imagination, I'm sure.

KNIGHT
Stick to your task. When will I see it?

DEVON
I tried to tell you. It'll be ready within the week.

KNIGHT
Excellent. I pray it leaves me enough time.

③

Typecast?

About the chapter

The extracts within this chapter are taken from radio, TV and a stage play, each displaying differences in layout and detail, according to their style. Each extract is taken from towards the end of the script, by which time characters have already been introduced and developed. This chapter focuses on how characters are further developed within a script to confirm or alter the audience's perception of them.

developing character

About the text

Sherlock Holmes is a famous private detective created by Arthur Conan Doyle and is a character who has been presented in a variety of stage and screen productions. He is well known for his superb powers of deduction and his belief that no villain can outwit him. The extract here is taken from a 1945 radio adaptation of *The Adventure of the Illustrious Client*, by Denis Green and Bruce Taylor, in which Holmes is, once again, displaying his super sleuth powers.

As you read this extract, consider the following features of the text:

Word level:

- How does the language of the script clearly establish that it is set in a different time?

Sentence level:

- How does the tone of the language used by Holmes differ from that of the other characters?

- Why is this?

Text level:

- What do you notice about the stage directions for this radio play extract?

- How do you think these might differ from those in a stage play extract?

- What differences would this make to an actor taking on the role of Holmes?

Previous page: Tony Stephens as Stanley Kowalski and Jessica Lange as Blanche DuBois in *A Streetcar Named Desire*.

The Adventure of the Illustrious Client

HOLMES
I think the identity of the murderer will be obvious when we find the jewels stolen from Madame Corvey's safe. Now the three people present at, or about, the time of the lady's murder were searched: myself – the Duc – and Mr Shipton here. Am I right, Inspector Charel?

CHAREL
Yes, monsieur, and the jewels were not found – so what does that prove?

HOLMES
One other person that had a motive for killing Madame Corvey was not searched – yourself, Inspector.

Excited buzz of voices.

CHAREL
[*Angrily.*] But this is outrageous! Are you accusing me?

Rap of gavel. Voices subside.

PREFECT
Monsieur Holmes, do you realize the significance of what you are implying?

HOLMES
I do, Monsieur le Prefect.

PREFECT
Very well then. Proceed.

HOLMES
Monsieur Charel, you stated that the beach gate was bolted. How did you find that out?

CHAREL
By trying it.

HOLMES
From inside – or outside?

CHAREL
From outside, of course.

HOLMES
I don't believe you. I think that when Doctor Watson telephoned your office you suspected where I might be going. You hurried ahead of the gendarmes and reached the Villa several minutes before I did. You found the beach gate was open … you saw Madame Corvey putting her jewels away, as Monsieur le Duc de Boncourt started to leave the room to go the cellar. You slipped through the windows, signalled to Madame Corvey, who was your confederate, to be silent … followed the Duc into the hall and struck him from behind. Then you went back into the library, killed Madame Corvey, and pocketed the jewels. You started to leave the front way … and saw me approaching. Seeing a chance to implicate me, you left the door ajar … and ran out the beach way, bolting the door behind you, and waited for your reinforcements.

CHAREL
You have convicted yourself! If you came to the villa after I was there – how could you have known what my movements were?

HOLMES
I admit that this part of my case is only supposition.

PREFECT
But Monsieur Holmes, that is no evidence.

CHAREL
Of course it is not!

HOLMES
Now I'll come to my facts. Doctor Watson, I wonder if you'd mind stepping forward?

WATSON
[*Fading in.*] I'm very glad to. In fact, I've been wondering why you haven't asked me to before, Holmes.

HOLMES

Will you please tell Monsieur le Prefect exactly what you did last night after I was brought here.

WATSON

With pleasure. [*Raising his voice slightly.*] Monsieur le Prefect, my old friend Mr Holmes told me to shadow Inspector Charel as soon as he left the Suretee* [*sic*] last night. And that's what I did … He walked down to the waterfront and entered a small café … I watched through the window and saw him give a package to a rough-looking sailor – and a few minutes later he left. Holmes had told me what to expect … so I followed the sailor. He went down to the wharf … I was behind him with a revolver in my pocket. As he started to get into a fishing boat … I captured him … and also these … .

Chatter of excited voices. Gavel.

HOLMES

You'll find, Monsieur Le Prefect, that those are the missing jewels.

CHAREL

That is a lie! He is lying to save his friend!

WATSON

Oh, no, I'm not! The fisherman is waiting outside the room now.

PREFECT

Have him brought in!

Footsteps. Chatter of voices.

HENRI

[*About fifty. French accent. Voluble.*] [*Fading in.*] Henri Borel has done nothing! Only what Monsieur Charel pays him to do … and now he is brought into the surette* [*sic*] like a criminal!

Commotion. Gavel. Voices subside.

PREFECT

Henri Borel … are those jewels the ones that were given to you by Monsieur Charel last night?

* Suretee and surette are mispronunciations of the French word Sûreté, which is the equivalent of the English CID.

HENRI
Oui, Monsieur le Prefect! But you must no blame me. I only do what I am told to do …
to sail with them to Corsica and give them to Monsieur Charel's brother. Just as I have
done a hundred times before.

CHAREL
[*Violently.*] He lies! I have never seen him in my life!

HENRI
I lie? Henri Baptiste Borel, born in your own home town of Ajaccio … I that have
known you since you were a boy? Sacré nom du chien, monsieur … what game do
you play?!

HOLMES
Monsieur le Prefect … the dagger on the table in front of you … may I show it to this
man?

PREFECT
Of course.

HOLMES
[*After a moment.*] Henri Borel … have you ever seen this dagger before?

HENRI
Mais oui! Of course I have seen it. My brother made it. He is the finest sword maker in
Ajaccio … he made it for Monsieur Charel … .

WATSON
[*Suddenly.*] Look out! Charel! He's drawing his revolver! Stop him!

Revolver shot.

Music: Up fast into bridge.

Footsteps on cobblestones.

WATSON
[*After footsteps are established.*] Well, Holmes, Charel solved it for you very simply by
committing suicide.

HOLMES
Oh, no, Watson, it was already solved … thanks to your very excellent sleuthing.

WATSON
[*Bumbling happily.*] I didn't do anything much. Holmes. Just what you told me to. By the way … I still don't understand Charel's motive for murdering Madame Corvey.

HOLMES
It was a combination of motives. Jealousy at her announcing her engagement to the Duc … and anger at realizing that she had replaced the jewels in Lord Shipton's heirloom without telling him. Henri Borel made it very clear tonight that they had been [in] partnership as smugglers for years.

WATSON
One of our most unusual cases. [*Facetiously.*] You know, Holmes, for a while, I was afraid you were going to end up in the guillotine!

HOLMES
[*Chuckling.*] Did you really, old fellow? By the way, there was a certain poetic justice about the case.

WATSON
In what way?!

HOLMES
Did you notice that Charel's dagger has an inscription on the blade?

WATSON
Yes … but I couldn't translate it.

HOLMES
It said: 'Che la mia ferita sia mortale.'

WATSON
And what does that mean, Holmes?

HOLMES
'Let my wound be mortal.'

Music: Up strong to curtain.

CAMPBELL
Tonight's Sherlock Holmes adventure is written by Denis Green and Bruce Taylor and is based on an incident in the Sir Arthur Conan Doyle story, *The Adventure of the Illustrious Client.*

About the text

A Streetcar Named Desire, by Tennessee Williams, is set in America in the 1940s and traces the troubled relationships between Blanche DuBois and her family and loved ones. The play shows Blanche finding it difficult to come to terms with a different lifestyle and, ultimately, her descent into madness. The extract here is taken from towards the end of the play, where Blanche has let her image slip and she is desperately trying to think back to happier times.

As you read this extract, consider the following features of the text:

Word level:

• How does Williams use particular words within the stage directions to create a vivid picture of Blanche within this extract?

Sentence level:

• Why do you think there is a shift from past to present tense in the stage directions?

Text level:

• How does the short speech by Blanche add to the information given in the stage directions?

• Why do you think Stanley, Blanche's brother-in-law, is introduced at the end of this section?

A Streetcar Named Desire

Scene 10

It is a few hours later that night. BLANCHE has been drinking fairly steadily since MITCH left. She has dragged her wardrobe trunk into the centre of the bedroom. It hangs open with flowery dresses thrown across it. As the drinking and packing went on, a mood of hysterical exhilaration came into her and she has decked herself out in a somewhat soiled and crumpled white satin evening gown and a pair of scuffed silver slippers with brilliants set in their heels. Now she is placing the rhinestone tiara on her head before the mirror of the dressing table and murmuring excitedly as if to a group of spectral admirers.

BLANCHE
How about taking a swim, a moonlight swim at the old rock quarry? If anyone's sober enough to drive a car! Ha–ha! Best way in the world to stop your head buzzing! Only you've got to be careful to dive where the deep pool is – if you hit a rock you don't come up till tomorrow … .

Trembling she lifts the hand mirror for a closer inspection. She catches her breath and slams the mirror face down with such violence that the glass cracks. She moans a little and attempts to rise. STANLEY appears around the corner of the building. He still has on the vivid green silk bowling shirt. As he rounds the corner the honky tonk music is heard. It continues softly throughout the scene. He enters the kitchen, slamming the door. As he peers in at BLANCHE, he gives a low whistle. He has had a few drinks on the way and has brought some quart beer bottles home with him.

About the text

The popular comedy series *Only Fools and Horses* is the subject of the third extract in this section. The series follows the antics of East End 'wide boy' Del and his brother Rodney as they struggle to make a living and dream of becoming millionaires. All of Del's schemes are somewhat shady, but he usually manages to stay out of trouble – just! In this extract, an old acquaintance, Slater, turns up, determined to get the better of Del.

As you read this extract, consider the following features of the text:

Word level:

- How does the screenwriter, John Sullivan, use particular words to convey the dialect of the main characters here?

Sentence level:

- What differences do you notice about the tone of the language used by Del compared with that used by Slater?

Text level:

- How do the audience's perceptions of Del alter as the extract progresses?

Only Fools and Horses

Del Boy, played by David Jason, and Uncle Albert, played by Buster Merryfield.

INT. NIGHT. CORRIDOR IN POLICE STATION.

RODNEY and GRANDAD are in the corridor. GRANDAD is seated directly below a 'Watch Out There's a Thief About' poster. He sees it and moves his chair closer to RODNEY.

GRANDAD
Why's he keeping Del Boy in there?

RODNEY
That is about the 38th time you've asked me that in the last 'alf hour! And for the 38th time Grandad, I'm telling you, I don't know!!

GRANDAD
I thought he'd just charge Del with receiving, he'd get a £50 fine and then it would all be forgot about!

RODNEY
That's what I thought!

GRANDAD
So did I! So why's he keeping him in there?

RODNEY
Gawd bless my old brown ... I don't bloody know Grandad!

GRANDAD
Well, Rodney … .

The door to the interview opens and HOSKINS looks out to see what all the noise is. RODNEY and GRANDAD smile nervously at him.

HOSKINS
Look, I thought I told you two you were free to go!

GRANDAD
Oh we thought we'd hang on a while.

RODNEY
Yeah, it's good here innit?

SLATER exits from the charge room carrying a piece of paper.

SLATER
Still here?

RODNEY
We're waiting for Del.

GRANDAD
Will he be long son?

SLATER
Only as long as it takes him to tell me who nicked the microwave.

RODNEY
Better get our head down till the morning then!

SLATER
Oh no, Del's seen the light. He's decided to cooperate.

GRANDAD
No, you're pulling our legs!

SLATER
D'you reckon? Well why don't you come in and see for yourselves? Come on.

INT. NIGHT. THE INTERVIEW ROOM.

DEL is seated at the table. SLATER enters followed by RODNEY and GRANDAD.

SLATER
Alright Hoskins, away you go, canteen's open now.

HOSKINS
Oh thank you very much, sir.

HOSKINS exits.

SLATER
[*Throws paper on desk*] There you are, Del Boy, your immunity from prosecution, signed by the Superintendent himself.

RODNEY
What are you playing at Del??!!

DEL
What are they doing 'ere?

SLATER
Oh, I thought it'd be interesting for them to see you in your real light. The Great Del Boy, the man who could talk his way out of a room with no doors, reduced to this, grassing!

DEL
I've got to tell him Rodney. He's got me all ends up ... I've got no choice.

GRANDAD
But you don't know his name Del, he was just a bloke in the market!

DEL
Oh leave it out Grandad. If Mr Slater was to believe our description he'd have had his men searching for someone who's a cross between Tom Thumb and the Jolly Green Giant!

SLATER
With a deaf-aid!

DEL
With a deaf-aid! Rodney, I wasn't doing it just for myself – he threatened to plant something on you, and set you up for a bit of bird!

RODNEY
But, but that's against the law!

SLATER
Well phone the police!

RODNEY
Don't tell him Del!

DEL
Look, I've got to Rodney, otherwise it'll mean you and me would go down the road and Grandad's going to be left alone on the estate, see I've got no choice, I've got no choice! Alright, Mr Slater, let's get down to business.

SLATER
Oh Del, Del Boy, those words are music to my ears. I will cherish this moment. Righto Del, who nicked it?

DEL
[*Indicating ROD and GRANDAD*] They are free to go ain't they?

SLATER
Yeah, they're free to go, no charges, they can leave whenever they like! OK give me his name?

DEL
And you've got nothing on me either?

SLATER
[*Losing his temper*] No! you've got an immunity from prosecution! You've got less chance of a pull than the Queen! [*DEL signs the paper*]

DEL
Long as I know!

SLATER
Right, for the third and the last time of asking, who nicked the microwave off the back of the lorry?

DEL looks anxiously at RODNEY and GRANDAD.

DEL
I did!

He smiles triumphantly at SLATER.

Close up on setting

About the chapter

This chapter focuses on descriptions of setting and building atmosphere within scripts and screenplays. The first extracts are taken from the original play and film adaptation of *Romeo and Juliet* and we then look at how atmosphere is built through setting and description in the film *The Sixth Sense*.

stage atmosphere, scene setting, scripting style

About the text

William Shakespeare's *Romeo and Juliet* is one of the most famous of all love stories, and tells the tale of two teenagers from feuding families, falling in love and eventually taking their own lives, as a result of conflict and a number of misunderstandings. In both extracts here, we see the first meeting of the two young lovers. The first extract is taken from the original play, and the second from Baz Luhrmann's film, co-written by himself and Craig Pearce, starring Leonardo Di Caprio and Claire Danes.

As you read these extracts, consider the following features of the text, or texts:

Word level:

- How does the film extract combine both the language of present day America, and that of Shakepeare's original play?

Sentence level:

- What do you notice about the sentence structures within the setting descriptions in the film extract?

Text level:

- What differences can you detect between the type of setting provided in the first extract (Shakespeare's original) and that of Luhrmann's film script?

- What differences would this make to a director preparing to present these versions on stage or screen?

- What differences would this make to an actor preparing for one of the main roles?

Previous page: a scene from the stage play *The Lion King*.

This page: Mujahid Kamal Khan as Romeo and Ruth D'Silva as Juliet.

ROMEO & JULIET

ACT I SCENE V

PETER and other SERVINGMEN come forth with napkins

PETER
Where's Potpan, that he helps not to take away?
He shift a trencher, he scrape a trencher!

FIRST SERVINGMAN
When good manners shall lie all in one or two men's hands, and they unwashed too, 'tis a foul thing.

PETER
Away with the joint-stools, remove the court-cupboard, look to the plate. Good thou, save me a piece of marzipan, and, as thou loves me, let the porter let in Susan Grindstone and Nell.
Anthony and Potpan!

SECOND SERVINGMAN
Ay, boy, ready.

PETER
You are looked for and called for, asked for
and sought for, in the great chamber.

FIRST SERVINGMAN
We cannot be here and there too. Cheerly,
boys! Be brisk a while, and the longest liver
take all.

*They come and go, setting forth tables and chairs.
Enter Musicians, then at one door CAPULET,
his WIFE, his COUSIN, JULIET, the NURSE,
TYBALT, his page, PETRUCCIO, and all the
guests and gentlewomen; at another door, the
masquers: ROMEO, BENVOLIO and
MERCUTIO.*

CAPULET
(*to the masquers*) Welcome, gentlemen.
Ladies that have their toes
Unplagued with corns will walk a bout with
you.
Aha, my mistresses, which of you all
Will now deny to dance? She that makes dainty,
She, I'll swear, hath corns. I am come near ye
now?
Welcome, gentlemen, I have seen the day
That I have worn a visor, and could tell
A whispering tale in a fair lady's ear
Such as would please. 'Tis gone, 'tis gone, 'tis
gone.
You are welcome, gentlemen. Come, musicians,
play.

*Music plays, and the masquers, guests, and
gentlewomen dance. ROMEO stands apart.*

A hall, a hall! Give room! and foot it, girls.

(*To SERVINGMEN*) More light, you knaves,
and turn the tables up,
And quench the fire, the room is grown too hot.
(*To his COUSIN*) Ah sirrah, this unlooked-for
sport comes well.
Nay, sit, nay, sit, good cousin Capulet,
For you and I are past our dancing days.

CAPULET and his COUSIN sit
How long is't now since last yourself and I
Were in a masque?

CAPULET'S COUSIN
By'r Lady, thirty years.

CAPULET
What, man, 'tis not so much, 'tis not so much.
'Tis since the nuptial of Lucentio,
Come Pentecost as quickly as it will,
Some five-and-twenty years; and then we
masqued.

CAPULET'S COUSIN
'Tis more, 'tis more. His son is elder, sir.
His son is thirty.

CAPULET
Will you tell me that?
His son was but a ward two years ago.

ROMEO
(*to a SERVINGMAN*) What lady's that which
doth enrich the hand
Of yonder knight?

SERVINGMAN
I know not, sir.

ROMEO
O, she doth teach the torches to burn bright!
It seems she hangs upon the cheek of night
As a rich jewel in an Ethiope's ear –
Beauty too rich for use, for earth too dear.
So shows a snowy dove trooping with crows
As yonder lady o'er her fellows shows.
The measure done, I'll watch her place of stand,
And, touching hers, make blessèd my rude hand.
Did my heart love till now? Forswear it, sight,
For I ne'er saw true beauty till this night.

TYBALT
This, by his voice, should be a Montague.
Fetch me my rapier, boy. (*Exit page*)
What, dares the slave
Come hither, covered with an antic face,
To fleer and scorn at our solemnity?
Now, by the stock and honour of my kin,
To strike him dead I hold it not a sin.

CAPULET
(*standing*) Why, how now, kinsman?
Wherefore storm you so?

TYBALT
Uncle, this is a Montague, our foe,
A villain that is hither come in spite
To scorn at our solemnity this night.

CAPULET
Young Romeo, is it?

TYBALT
'Tis he, that villain Romeo.

CAPULET
Content thee, gentle coz, let him alone.
A bears him like a portly gentleman,
And, to say truth, Verona brags of him
To be a virtuous and well-governed youth.
I would not for the wealth of all this town
Here in my house do him disparagement.
Therefore be patient, take no note of him.
It is my will, the which if thou respect,
Show a fair presence and put off these frowns,
And ill-beseeming semblance for a fcast.

TYBALT
It fits when such a villain is a guest.
I'll not endure him.

CAPULET
He shall be endured.
What, goodman boy, I say he shall. Go to,
Am I the master here or you? Go to –
You'll not endure him! God shall mend my soul.
You'll make a mutiny among my guests,
You will set cock-a-hoop! You'll be the man!

TYBALT
Why, uncle, 'tis a shame.

CAPULET
Go to, go to,
You are a saucy boy. Is't so, indeed?
This trick may chance to scathe you. I know what,
You must contrary me. Marry, 'tis time –

*A dance ends. JULIET retires to her place of
stand, where ROMEO awaits her*

(*To the guests*) Well said, my hearts!
(*To TYBALT*) You are a princox, go.
Be quiet, or – (*to SERVINGMEN*) more light,
more light! –
(*To TYBALT*) for shame,
I'll make you quiet. (*To the guests*) What,
cheerly, my hearts!

The music plays again and the guests dance

TYBALT
Patience perforce with wilful choler meeting
Makes my flesh tremble in their different
greeting.
I will withdraw, but this intrusion shall,
Now seeming sweet, convert to bitt'rest gall.

Exit

ROMEO
(*to JULIET, touching her hand*)
If I profane with my unworthiest hand
This holy shrine, the gentler sin is this:
My lips, two blushing pilgrims, ready stand
To smooth that rough touch with a tender kiss.

JULIET
Good pilgrim, you do wrong your hand too
much,
Which mannerly devotion shows in this.
For saints have hands that pilgrims' hands do
touch,
And palm to palm is holy palmers' kiss.

ROMEO
Have not saints lips, and holy palmers, too?

JULIET
Ay, pilgrim, lips that they must use in prayer.

ROMEO
O then, dear saint, let lips do what hands do:
They pray; grant thou, lest faith turn to despair.

JULIET
Saints do not move, though grant for
prayers' sake.

ROMEO
Then move not while my prayer's effect I take.

He kisses her

Thus from my lips, by thine my sin is purged.

JULIET
Then have my lips the sin that they have took.

ROMEO
Sin from my lips? O trespass sweetly urged!
Give me my sin again.

He kisses her

JULIET
You kiss by th' book.

NURSE
Madam, your mother craves a word with you.

JULIET departs to her mother.

WILLIAM SHAKESPEARE'S ROMEO & JULIET

INT. CAPULET'S MANSION – BALLROOM. NIGHT.

PULL OUT: *To discover the glittering dots of fire refracting from the sparkling domed roof of the magnificently ornate CAPULET Ballroom. The camera swoops down over bizarrely costumed revellers cavorting to a driving Latin big band. The camera partners with a drugged MERCUTIO and BENVOLIO who shamelessly caper with each other in a mock antic adagio.*

CUT TO: ROMEO *gazing blankly at the dance floor.*

CUT TO: MERCUTIO. *He sweeps up a thirty-something sophisticate and twirls her in* ROMEO'S *direction.*

> MERCUTIO
> Everyman betake him to his legs!

> ROMEO *moves off through the crowd.*

> CUT TO: ROMEO'S P.O.V.: *Contorted images of costumed guests eat, drink and laugh in a grotesque collision of Yves Saint Laurent cocktail party and Bacchanalian romp.*

> *Suddenly a large arm coils around* ROMEO'S *neck.*

> DISTORTED EXTREME CLOSE UP: *A seriously intoxicated FULGENCIO CAPULET; his puffy red face squeezes against* ROMEO'S.

> CAPULET
> Ah, I have seen the day that I could
> Tell a whispering tale in a fair lady's ear.
> Such as would please.

> CAPULET *screams above the music:*

CUT TO	abrupt change of shot
P.O.V.	point of view
PULL OUT	camera moves out

CAPULET [CONT.]
Come musicians play!

Blood drums in ROMEO'S ears. Breaking free from CAPULET'S grasp as he pushes through the crowd toward the bathroom.

INT. BATHROOM. NIGHT.

Silent, underwater shot. ROMEO'S tranquil features submerged in a basin of water.

BEAT.

With a gasp, ROMEO rises. A moment. His breathing calms. Then, smoothing water into his hair, he gazes into the bathroom mirror. He turns:

The entire wall opposite the mirror is a magnificent salt-water fish tank.

ROMEO, drawn by its submarine beauty, leans against the fish tank. Applause echoes faintly through the bathroom speakers.

INT. BALLROOM. NIGHT.

As the applause dies, a dark-haired Latina Diva takes the spotlight. The band ease into the opening bars of a love ballad.

INT. BATHROOM. NIGHT.

As the music swells, ROMEO watches a moustached catfish glide past a medieval castle.

Suddenly, ROMEO pulls away. Peering back at him through the castle is a pair of exquisitely beautiful angelic eyes.

The Diva's first pure, achingly beautiful notes soar.

Confused, ROMEO looks again. There is no mistake – it is a girl. Through a shimmering curtain of ribbon weed, two dark wide eyes, a childish nose and sumptuous full lips.

ROMEO pushes his face closer to the glass. The other face snaps abruptly away.

INT. POWDER ROOM. NIGHT.

CUT TO: JULIET, dressed as an angel, on the other side of the tank. We now realise that the girls' powder room and the boys' bathroom are divided by this watery wonder world.

JULIET warily moves closer to the glass.

INT. BATHROOM. NIGHT.

ROMEO leans his face against the glass. The love ballad builds.

SLOW TRACK: From ROMEO'S profile, in through the water, and …

INT. POWDER ROOM. NIGHT.

… out the other side, to find JULIET in profile, peering into the tank.

INT. BATHROOM. NIGHT.

ROMEO presses his nose lightly against the glass.

INT. POWDER ROOM. NIGHT.

JULIET: a tiny smile.

Suddenly, CRASH! The door slams open. JULIET turns, startled. It is the NURSE.

NURSE
Juliet, your mother calls.

The NURSE bustles JULIET out the door. JULIET looks over her shoulder at the mystery boy.

INT. BALLROOM. NIGHT.

ROMEO, now without his mask, slams out of the bathroom – JULIET and the NURSE have disappeared into the crowd.

CUT TO: JULIET being dragged along by the NURSE. She glances back toward the mystery boy, but he is gone.

JULIET and the NURSE rejoin DAVE PARIS, who is dressed as an astronaut, and GLORIA, at the side of the dance floor.

DAVE, irresistible smile, extends his hand to JULIET.

DAVE
Will you now deny to dance?

JULIET looks to DAVE, desperately searching for a reason to decline. GLORIA, brushing aside her silly daughter's protests, slugs the last of her champagne and corrals them onto the dance floor.

GLORIA
[*whispering to JULIET*] A man, young lady, such a man.

As JULIET is dragged onto the floor, her eyes furtively search for the boy.

CUT TO: ROMEO in the crowd. Desperate to find the girl, he roughly shunts aside a reveller dressed as Lucifer, Prince of Darkness.

HOLD ON: Lucifer. He removes his mask: it is TYBALT. He turns to ABRA, who's dressed as a demon.

TYBALT
What, dares the slave come hither
to fleer and scorn at our solemnity?
Now by the stock and honor of my kin
To strike him dead I hold it not a sin.

TYBALT moves off aggressively, but is halted as CAPULET slams a hand into his chest.

CAPULET
Why how now kinsman, wherefore
storm you so?

TYBALT
Uncle, this is that villain Romeo.
A Montague, our foe.

CAPULET peers across the ballroom.

CAPULET
Young Romeo is it?

TYBALT
'Tis he.

CAPULET
Content thee gentle coz, let him alone.
I would not for the wealth of all this town
Here in my house do him disparagement.
Therefore be patient; take no note of him.

TYBALT can't believe it.

HOLD ON camera focused on

SLOW TRACK camera follows slowly

atmosphere, setting, style

TYBALT
I'll not endure him.

CLOSE ON: CAPULET, exploding with rage.

CAPULET
He shall be endured!
[*slapping TYBALT viciously*]
What, goodman boy! I say he shall!
Go to.

CAPULET violently shoves TYBALT to the ground.

CAPULET
You'll make a mutiny among my guests!

A middle aged couple look on shocked – CAPULET waves to them festively:

CAPULET
What? Cheerly my hearts!

CAPULET snorts at TYBALT in disgust.

CAPULET
You'll not endure him! Am I the
master here or you? Go to.

Smoothing his hair into place, CAPULET turns back into the ballroom.

CLOSE ON: TYBALT choking back tears of rage.

CUT TO: ROMEO moving through the crowd. For a moment the crush clears and he spies the Angel on the dance floor.

CLOSE ON: ROMEO whispers:

ROMEO
Did my heart love till now?
Forswear it, sight.
For I ne'er saw true beauty till
this night.

ROMEO begins to circumnavigate the dance floor in an attempt to get closer to JULIET.

CUT TO: DAVE slow-dancing with JULIET.

JULIET'S eyes search the room for the boy.

CLOSE ON: ROMEO.

CLOSE ON: JULIET.

Their eyes connect.

JULIET looks quickly back to DAVE who, oblivious, returns his most devastating smile.

CUT TO: The songstress, her voice soars.

CUT TO: JULIET. Unable to look away from the boy, she stares over DAVE'S shoulder.

CUT TO: ROMEO. Ignoring the danger, he continues to move toward the Angel.

With the Diva's spiralling final notes, the ballad concludes.

A complete blackout. As the crowd break into wild applause, JULIET'S eyes search the darkness, but the boy is gone.

The crowd cheers and screams its applause. An avalanche of balloons, tinsel and confetti rains down from the roof; swathes of red silk drop from the ceiling and the space is transformed.

CLOSE ON: JULIET, searching for the boy.

Suddenly: A gasp, JULIET'S eyes widen, shocked.

In the dark, a hand has shot out from the drape curtaining off the stage and clasped hers. JULIET barely dares breathe.

She glances furtively to DAVE PARIS – he watches the stage.

Slowly JULIET turns toward the hand; there through a break in the curtain she can see eye, cheek and lips of the mystery boy. As the Diva reprises the chorus, ROMEO gently pulls JULIET behind the curtain.

INT. BEHIND CURTAIN. NIGHT.

Concealed from the party by the red velvet drape, hands still clasped, the teenagers are so close their bodies almost touch.

Cole Seer, played by Haley Joel Osment in *The Sixth Sense*.

About the text

The mystery thriller *The Sixth Sense*, written and directed by M Night Shyamalan, follows the actions of an analyst who is treating a young child, Cole, haunted by ghosts and troubled spirits. Cole realises he is a point of contact for these spirits and that he has a role to play in resolving issues for them. In this extract, Cole attends the funeral of a young girl and, with her guidance, finds evidence of wrongdoing on the part of her stepmother. The original American spelling has been retained.

As you read this extract, consider the following features of the text:

Word level:

- How does the screenwriter use particular words to combine the innocence of childhood with a more sinister mood?

Sentence level:

- How does the variety of sentence structures in the setting descriptions help build up a tense atmosphere in this scene?

Text level:

- What different images of despair and pain are created here?

- How is the presentation of the stepmother similar to other stories you know or have read?

The Sixth Sense

INT. GIRL'S BEDROOM – AFTERNOON

COLE closes the door behind him. He turns and gazes at the GIRL'S bedroom. There's a hospital bed near the window. The walls are covered with get-well cards and drawings from family, friends, and school children.

Her shelves are filled with puppets. All shapes and sizes of puppets. Next to the shelf is a puppet stage and a camcorder on a mini tripod sitting next to it.

COLE walks to the shelf and picks up a FINGER PUPPET DANCER. He places it in his pocket.

On the GIRL'S desk, is a large collection of video cassettes. The labels read, 'Puppet Show Christmas 96,' 'Puppet Show Birthday party,' 'Puppet Show class trip'… .

COLE reads the labels carefully before moving towards the closets. He passes the bed.

AN EMACIATED HAND REACHES OUT FROM BENEATH THE BED AND GRABS COLE'S ANKLE.

COLE jerks back startled. He watches as the GIRL'S hand slips back under the bed. COLE stays very still. Waits. Nothing happens.

He slowly bends down. His hands touch the floor. He tilts his head and looks under the bed.

The emaciated little GIRL who came to his tent lays curled on the floor. Her bulging eyes glare at COLE. She moves suddenly. Thrusts a jewelry box forward. It slides across the wooden floor and stops just before COLE. COLE and the sickly GIRL stare at each other. Neither of them say a word.

CUT TO:

INT. LIVING ROOM – AFTERNOON

The room is thick with mourners. Most are gathered around the GIRL'S MOTHER, a young woman in her late twenties. As she moves through the room to the kitchen, she receives the many cards, hugs, and flowers that are offered as condolence. MRS COLLINS leaves the living room.

MALCOLM watches breathlessly from the doorway as COLE moves through the many adults across the room.

The GIRL'S FATHER, MR COLLINS, a thin man in his late twenties, is seated on the reading chair next to a TV. His face is granite. No one in the room dares to talk to him. He stares statue-like at an abstract point in the room.

COLE

Mister?

The man doesn't react. Some of the guests look oddly at the little boy standing before the man.

COLE

Excuse me, Mister.

Beat. The man slowly turns and looks down at the boy standing next to him. COLE is very shaky.

MALCOLM watches everything anxiously.

COLE stares at MR COLLINS.

COLE

Are you Kyra's daddy?

The man's face begins to crumble. Beat. He nods, 'yes' softly.

COLE holds out the jewelry box. It trembles with his hands.

The FATHER just stares at it. Beat.

COLE

It's for you ...

[*beat*]

she wanted to tell you something.

The FATHER becomes very still. His eyes fill with a storm of confusion and pain. After the longest time, the FATHER reaches and gently takes the box out of COLE'S small hands.

COLE begins to back away ... .

The FATHER gazes at COLE as he melts into the crowd. COLE reaches MALCOLM and the two then slip out of the house.

The FATHER looks down in a daze. He goes to open the jewelry box. His movements are slow and strained. He lifts the latch and opens the box.

MR COLLINS stares at an unlabeled video cassette.

CUT TO:

INT. LIVING ROOM – AFTERNOON

People in the room start to turn as the TV comes on. MR COLLINS is seated now.

THE STATIC SNOW ON THE SCREEN IS QUICKLY REPLACED BY AN IMAGE. TWO PUPPETS DANCE ON STAGE. WE HEAR KYRA'S VOICE SING FOR THE PUPPETS AS THEY DANCE AROUND.

Her FATHER'S face forms the most heartbreaking of smiles as he watches the performance.

The entire room has stopped what they were doing.

TV SCREEN

WE HEAR FOOTSTEPS COMING UP THE STAIRS. The puppets go limp. The entire stage gets lifted up. We see it carried away by KYRA. We can view the whole bedroom now. The camera is seated on her desk in the corner.

KYRA climbs in bed and pretends to be sleeping when the door opens. It's MRS COLLINS. She carries in a tray of soup and a sandwich.

LIVING ROOM

The crowd watches in riveted silence. The FATHER never takes his eyes off of the screen.

The image of the MOTHER prepares the meal. She uncovers the fruit and the soup. Places a straw into the drink.

And then it happens.

The image of the MOTHER walks to a closet. Opens it. An assortment of household cleaners and sponges are kept inside. She pulls out a bottle of floor cleaner. Reads the label for the ingredients. Walks back to the food tray, where she unscrews the cap on the floor cleaner. The MOTHER pours some into the cap.

Checks it.

MRS COLLINS

[*video tape*] That's too much.

The MOTHER pours some into the bottle. The remainder goes into the child's soup. She replaces the cap and puts the bottle back in the closet.

The image of the MOTHER turns to the bed carrying the tray. She places the food on a metallic rolling table and swings it over the bed.

MRS COLLINS

[*video tape*] Kyra, time for lunch.

KYRA pretends to wake from a deep sleep.

KYRA

[*video tape*] I'm feeling much better now.

The image of the MOTHER smiles.

MRS COLLINS

[*video tape*] I'm glad, honey.

[*beat*]

Time for your food.

KYRA

[*video tape*] Can I go outside, if I eat this?

MRS COLLINS

[*video tape*] We'll see. You know how you get sick in the afternoon.

KYRA picks up the spoon and takes a sip. Her face crinkles at the taste. She looks up at her MOTHER.

MRS COLLINS

[*video tape*] Don't say it tastes funny. You know I don't like to hear that.

KYRA slowly brings the spoon to her mouth and swallows another spoonful.

The FATHER SHUTS OFF THE TELEVISION with his trembling hands. He presses his hands to his eyes like they're burning.

The ROOM IS UTTERLY SILENT.

CUT TO:

INT. DINING ROOM – AFTERNOON

MRS COLLINS is seated at the dining room surrounded by friends and family. She fixes one of the many bouquets of flowers on the table. It takes her a beat before she feels the stare.

She looks up.

Standing in the doorway to the dining room is MR COLLINS. A group of ashen faced guests stand in the distance behind him.

Husband and wife's eyes meet. MRS COLLINS smiles softly. MR COLLINS' eyes tremble with tears.

MR COLLINS

[*soft*] You were keeping her sick ... .

The whole world stops.

The MOTHER'S face registers confusion at first. Then slow realization. Her eyes glace at the many faces around her.

She looks back at her husband. His glare is painful. Rage filling every cell of his body. Tears falling faster down his cheeks.

MRS COLLINS turns her attention back to the flowers. She concentrates with all her strength. Beat. Her hands begin to shake.

MRS COLLINS

[*to no one*] I took care of her ... .

Her words are met with ice cold stares. The first tears stream down her face. The pretty flowers of consolation in her hand tumble to the floor.

5

The plot unfolds

About the chapter

The extracts in this chapter focus on how the narrative (the story or sequence of events) in scripts is developed. The extracts are taken from a range of media – stage, radio, film – and show key moments when the writers attempt to convey to the audience how events are developing. This understanding can be made explicit, or can be conveyed more subtly.

developing narratives

About the text

Frankenstein, a novel written by Mary Shelley in 1818, is considered to be one of the first horror stories. It depicts a man attempting to create human life, and there have been many film adaptations of it. In this 1999 film adaptation, *Mary Shelley's Frankenstein*, directed by and starring Kenneth Branagh, we see Victor Frankenstein in a frenzy of creation and subsequently feeling the despair that follows. Bear in mind the idea that Frankenstein wanted to create a thing of beauty and, in that sense, he was pursuing a Romantic ideal.

As you read this extract, consider the following features of the text:

Word level:

- Which words and phrases create the image of creation and birth?

Sentence level:

- How does the screenwriter use a variety of sentence structures to build up the dramatic tension of this extract?

Text level:

- Why does the narrative in this scene move Victor from despair to triumph and back to despair again?

- At which moments do these changes occur?

Frankenstein

Extract from the film

VICTOR
No, no, no!

Slowly he turns and walks away, his experiment, all his work, a failure.

We move slowly in on the porthole by the Creature's hand. It taps on the glass. Inside the sarcophagus the Creature's eyes open – and register panic.

VICTOR, hearing the noise, turns. Is he imagining it?

The sarcophagus begins to convulse.

VICTOR
It's alive, It's alive ... .

He races towards the sarcophagus, which is now shaking madly, and reaches out to the main lock. But before he can get to the lead bolts, they snap from the power inside the sarcophagus.

Suddenly the lid flies off, sending VICTOR backwards into the spill tank as a wave of fluid lands on him.

The lid of the sarcophagus flies through the lab, sending shelves and equipment flying, finally ending up near the door, having knocked the shelf holding VICTOR'S coat onto the ground.

VICTOR stares aghast at the sarcophagus. Slowly he gets to his feet and walks towards the now motionless vat. He walks up to the side of it, looking in, anticipating his creation is alive. But everything is still, no sign of life.

He looks down towards the feet – and suddenly the Creature flies up in front of him, grabbing for him. As he does this, the sarcophagus starts to topple off its rail and tips over onto its side, sending VICTOR and the Creature flying across the spill tank amongst the fluid and eels.

Slowly VICTOR looks up as the Creature crawls through the fluid.

VICTOR
I knew it could work. I knew it!

He moves over to his creation and tries to lift him to his feet. The Creature seems as helpless as the newly born.

VICTOR
Stand, please stand, come on ... .

The Creature, his vision hazy, manages to get to his feet.

VICTOR
[*monologue during the following action*]
Breathe, come on breathe.
Stand, you can stand, come on, come on, that's it.
What's wrong? What's wrong with you?
That's it, that's it.

You can do it, come on.

Stand, yes. Now walk. No, no.

With VICTOR still on his knees, they then slowly slide across the tank, the Creature managing to stand some of the time.

VICTOR
Let me help you, I'll help you to stand – the chains, the chains, over here.

VICTOR leads him over to some chains hanging from a bar and, in an attempt to help him to stand, he fits the Creature's arms into some ropes.

VICTOR
This must work, you're alive. What is wrong? What's wrong with you? Be careful of the rope – look out!

As VICTOR steps back, he loses his balance and, falling backwards, grabs a rope. A counterweight snaps, overloading the pulley, and the wooden bar of chains begins to rise up, carrying the Creature with it, moaning and twitching.

A piece of wood comes down past him and hits him over the head. The bar of chains continues to rise and the Creature continues to struggle.

VICTOR stands, dripping fluid and goo, chest heaving, staring up at the Creature. The full horror sinks in.

Now the Creature's death throes are complete.

Silence. Softly:

VICTOR
It's dead, it's dead, I've killed it! [*pause*]
What have I done? I gave it life and then I killed it.

About the text

The radio play *Zero Hour* was adapted from Ray Bradbury's story and was originally broadcast in 1955, when people were concerned about invasions from other worlds. This coincided with the first steps towards space exploration, and also with uncertainty about world peace, resulting from difficult relations between the United States and what was then called the Soviet Union. In the extract here, the young child Mink has been playing strangely throughout the day and talking about a character called 'Drill'. Mink's mother becomes concerned about her antics, and the scene begins with a worried telephone call. As the extract progresses, it is clear this is not simply children playing a harmless game. The original American spelling of the text has been retained.

As you read, consider the following features of the text:

Word level:

- Which words in the script point to this being written and performed in a different era?

Sentence level:

- What differences are there between the way Mary (Mink's mother) speaks and the way Henry (Mink's father) speaks? Why do you think this is?

Text level:

- Why do you think the radio announcer adds information to complement the dialogue of the characters?

- Do you think this is an effective device?

Zero Hour

MUSIC UP and UNDER

ANNOUNCER

It was a game called 'Invasion'. Mrs Morris' little girl, Mink, was playing it. So was Mink's friend, Anna, and all the other children under eleven. It was called 'Invasion'. And Zero Hour was to be at five o'clock. Mrs Morris was disturbed. She wasn't sure why ... but there was something ... something about parents shutting ears and eyes to what was happening. And because she was disturbed, she did something she didn't usually do – she called her husband at the office.

HENRY

[*filter*] Hello, dear.

MARY

Oh, hello, Henry. I'm sorry to bother you, but Miss Maxson said you weren't busy.

HENRY

Oh, not too. I should be able to get home early today. Everything alright?

MARY

Yes.

HENRY

You alright?

MARY

I ... I'm fine.

HENRY

Mink?

MARY

Oh, she's ... Henry?

HENRY

What?

MARY

Oh, ah ... nothing. I just wanted to talk to you for a minute ... that's all.

HENRY

[*laughs*] Listen, are you sure you're alright?

MARY

Oh, yes.

HENRY

Mink been getting on your nerves?

MARY

N ... not really.

HENRY

Well you tell her to behave or when I get home she and I are gonna have a talk. As a matter of fact, she's been a little fresh lately and I don't think it's good.

MARY

Well, she's playing outside. She's fine.

HENRY

Honey, is something wrong?

MARY

Why, no, I told you I ... I was thinking about you and wanted to talk, that's all. Nothing wrong with that.

HENRY

Not a thing.

FILTER muffled

MUSIC UP and UNDER music becomes louder and continues in the background

---

MARY
You go back to your work, dear. I'll see you soon.

HENRY
Alright.

MARY
What time do you think you'll be home?

HENRY
Oh, 'bout five ... maybe a little earlier.

MARY
Five. Oh ... .

HENRY
Hey, what? Come on, what?

MARY
Well, I ... I was just thinking ... nothing really, just Mink and you and me. Goodbye, dear.

HENRY
You *are* okay aren't you?

MARY
Yes I'm fine, goodbye.

HENRY
Goodbye.

F/X: PHONE HANGS UP

MUSIC UP AND OUT

ANNOUNCER
Another hour passed and it was half past four. The day began to wane. The sun lowered in a peaceful blue sky. Shadows lengthened on the green lawn. Outside it was quiet. The two little girls more intent than ever upon their endless movement of design and pattern with the implements before them. Mrs Morris watched from the window and she had never known Mink to have such powers of concentration. She had turned on the radio and sat drinking a cup of coffee and turned over her thoughts.

F/X: RADIO MUSIC in B/G

F/X: COFFEE CUP CLINKING

MARY
Children. Children. Children. Love and hate side by side. Sometimes children love you, hate you, all in half a second. Strange, children. Do they ever forget or forgive the whippings and the harsh strict words of command? I wonder? I wonder? How can you forget or forgive those over and above you? Those tall, silly dictators. Those ... parents.

MINK
[*calling from off mic*] Mom?

F/X: SPOON DROPS on COFFEE CUP

MARY
[*startled*] Oh, what is it, dear?

MINK
[*off mic*] Have we got a piece of lead pipe and a hammer?

MARY
Well, I ... I don't know. There might be in the garage. What do you want them for?

MINK
[*off mic*] We just need them.

MARY
Well, if you tell me what for, dear, maybe I can ... .

MINK
[*off mic*] I can get them. Thanks, Mom.

MARY
Is ... is something wrong?

B/G	background
F/X	sound effects

MINK

[*off mic*] Drill's stuck halfway and if we can get him all the way through it'd be easier. Then all the others can come through after him.

MARY

Well, can I help?

MINK

[*off mic*] Thanks, Mom, I can fix it.

MARY

You better get through, Mink. I want you to take your bath before your father comes home

MINK

[*off mic*] Awright.

MARY

Now he's coming home early. And Mink ... Mink ... .

ANNOUNCER

Mink had disappeared behind the shrubs and Mrs Morris knew it was ridiculous to make an issue of it. Besides, what was the issue? Invasion? Drill? Zero Hour? Unaccountably, a cool breeze came up. And although normally for that time of year, would have been relief, Mrs Morris felt a chill. She closed the window.

F/X: Window CLOSES

MUSIC UP and OUT

ANNOUNCER

Time passed. A curious waiting silence came upon the street. Deepening. Then from the living room, Mrs Morris heard ... .

F/X: MANTLE CLOCK STRIKES FIVE O'CLOCK

ANNOUNCER

Five o'clock. Zero hour. It had come. And now it had gone. But was the clock right? Mrs Morris, knowing how foolish it was, knowing it – went to the phone and dialed.

F/X: PHONE DIALS

MARY

[*under dialing*] Ah, silly. It's silly.

F/X: PHONE RINGS ON LINE

OPERATOR

When you hear the tone the time will be exactly four fifty-four and twenty seconds.

F/X: PHONE BEEP

MUSIC UP

ANNOUNCER

Four fifty-four and twenty seconds and Mrs Morris knew it wasn't as silly as she thought. Because it wasn't five o'clock yet. Not Zero Hour yet. Then the car drove up into the driveway.

F/X: CAR STOPPING

following dialog happens off mic

HENRY

Hi, Mink. How's it going? Hi, Anna.

MINK

Hi, Daddy.

ANNA

Hi, Mr Morris.

MINK

Fine.

HENRY

Got a kiss for your old man?

MINK

Haven't got time now, Daddy.

HENRY

Well that's a nice thing. What are you doing?

MINK
We're playing Invasion.

HENRY
Oh, swell. Your mother in the house?

MINK
Uh-huh.

HENRY
Okay, be good.

MINK
I will. Zero Hour in a few minutes, Daddy.

HENRY
[*chuckling*] Alright, I'll be ready.

MUSIC UP

ANNOUNCER
Mrs Morris heard him chuckle. Then his steps up the walk to the front door.

F/X: FOOTSTEPS on concrete

F/X: KEYS IN DOOR. DOOR OPENS

HENRY
[*calling*] Mary.

F/X: DOOR CLOSES

MARY
I'm in the living room, dear.

HENRY
Oh, hi. Our daughter didn't have time for a kiss. How about you?

F/X: KISS

MOTHER
[*nervous laugh*] Hard day?

HENRY
Not particularly.

MARY
Would you like a cocktail?

F/X: FOOTSTEPS to get drinks

HENRY
You read my mind.

MARY
Martini?

F/X: MAKING A MARTINI

HENRY
Perfect. Anything exciting happen today?

MARY
No. Oh, Helen called. From Danbury. I … I told her she was crazy, but she just felt like calling.

HENRY
Like you calling me this afternoon – crazy, huh? Hey, what was that all about?

MARY
Well, I told you. I … I just wanted to.

HENRY
Hum. Hey, incidentally, what's this new game the kids are playing – Invasion. That's a nice depressing thought. [*pause*] Is she alright? Come to think of it, she looked kind of funny.

MARY
She's alright. What's the time, Henry?

HENRY
A couple of minutes after five. Why?

MARY
No, no, the clock's wrong. By your watch.

HENRY
Oh, I've got two minutes to. I'm probably slow. You got something on the stove?

MARY
No, I … I just wondered.

HENRY
Honey, hey, look at me. What's the matter?

MARY
Nothing, really.

HENRY
Now … .

MARY
Really!

HENRY
Mink's been up to something … .

MARY
No, of course not … .

HENRY
Then what?

MARY
I … I guess I'm … a little tired. Upset, that's all.

HENRY
You want to go out for dinner?

MARY
Oh, no, I've … got a … steak here.

HENRY
I'll tell you what, I'll barbeque. How'll that be?

MARY
Oh, fine [*starting to panic*] Wha … what was that!

HENRY
What?

MARY
Well, I … thought I heard something.

HENRY
Well, I didn't.

MARY
I must have been imagining it.

HENRY
Hey you are jumpy. Why don't you have a drink, it'll do you good.

MARY
No, I don't want one. What's the time!

HENRY
[*getting annoyed*] Mary, what is this? Now I mean it. Something's wrong and I want to know.

MARY
It's silly. It's … so silly. I'm on edge, that's all.

HENRY
Mary.

MARY
I am!

HENRY
I don't like this. That kid's done something hasn't she? I'm gonna get her in here … .

MARY
No, no, Henry please don't! She hasn't. It's nothing at all. I just … .

F/X: HUMMING BEGINS and continues UNDER

HENRY
What's that?

MOTHER
I … I don't … know.

HENRY
Those kids haven't got anything dangerous out there have they? I noticed a lot of junk lying around.

MOTHER
[*tentative laugh*] I … I thought it was a game. She wouldn't have done it herself. [*beginning to get hysterical*] They made her do it!

F/X: BUMP HUM

HENRY
What the devil!

MOTHER
[*more hysterical*] Maybe you better go out and tell her to stop playing now.

It's after five! You tell Mink to put off the invasion until tomorrow.

HENRY
It's coming from outside. What are they up to? I'd better take a look!

F/X: FOOTSTEPS

HENRY
Mink! Mink!

F/X: EXPLOSION

HENRY
Good Lord!

MOTHER
Oh, ah!

F/X: EXPLOSIONS UNDER THE FOLLOWING

HENRY
Bombs! Bombs! They're bombing!

MARY
No, no, it's upstairs. I know it is. In the attic. That's where it is.

MUSIC UP and OUT

F/X: TWO SETS of FOOTSTEPS RUNNING

HENRY
Mary, Mary it is not up there!

ANNOUNCER
He ran after her confused, not a little frightened. She seemed to know something.

MOTHER
In the attic.

ANNOUNCER
Her mind had worked that quickly. Any excuse to get him away from the outside – to get him upstairs to the attic in time. And outside there were more explosions and they could hear the children screaming with delight.

HENRY
It is not in the attic, it's outside! Mink's out there! What's the matter with you?

F/X: FOOTSTEPS STOP

MARY
[*she is now hysterical*] No, no, I'll show you! Hurry! Get inside quick!

F/X: DOOR CLOSES and LOCKS

MARY breathes heavily and moans in panic under the following. She is now practically crazed.

MARY
Now we're safe until the night.

HENRY
Are you crazy! Why'd you throw that key away!?

MARY
Maybe we can sneak out later! Maybe we can escape!

HENRY
For heaven's sake! the kid's out there! Do you want her to get ki … .

MARY
Oh, no, no, you don't know, you don't. We've got to stay here, we've got to. It's horrible! We've got to, you've got to stay here with me.

HENRY
At this point I don't know how the devil I can get out! Where's that light … .

MARY
Be quiet, please, be quiet. they'll hear us, they'll find us. Henry please.

F/X: PHONE RINGS

HENRY
Well who's going to answer the telephone?

F/X: HUMMING BEGINS and PHONE CONTINUES TO RING [*MARY is crying in terror throughout*]

HENRY
There's that noise again! It's in this house! Mary what is this? Mary what's happening? You know, now answer me!

MARY
[*she continues her cry of fright*]

HENRY
Stop it, Mary, stop it! Somebody's downstairs! Who's down there? Who?

MARY
Oh, no, no, no, no, no, no. Oh, hush, please, please be quiet. They might go away, please, please.

MUSIC STING

ANNOUNCER
Between his wife's terror and the electric humming from below, Mr Morris felt a great fear. They trembled together in silence in the attic. Mr and Mrs Morris – parents of the little girl. Then they heard steps coming up up the stairs …

F/X: FOOTSTEPS on STAIRS

ANNOUNCER
… and a voice.

MINK
[*calling sweetly almost singing*] Mommy. Daddy. Where are you?

ANNOUNCER
And a queer cold light became visible under the door crack. The strange odor and the alien sound of eagerness in Mink's voice was almost more than they could bear. Each wanted to scream.

F/X: HUMM BUMP

> **MUSIC STING** a short musical phrase, used between one moment and another

MINK
Mommy. Daddy.

ANNOUNCER
And another sound … .

F/X: LASER SOUND ATTACKING DOOR LOCK

ANNOUNCER
And the attic lock … melted.

we hear whimpering of MARY and HENRY

ANNOUNCER
Mink. Mink with bright little eyes and tousled hair, peered inside. And behind her, tall, wavering blue shadows, frightful shadows.

MINK
Peek a boo.

MARY and HENRY
[*bloodcurdling screams*]

END MUSIC UP

About the text

The Granny Project, a stage play based on her own novel by Anne Fine, tells the story of a family dealing with a sick elderly relative, which causes problems for the younger members of this family. In these two extracts, we are introduced to Nicholas, who acts almost as a narrator in the play, talking directly to the audience about the different characters and what has happened.

As you read these extracts, consider the following features of the text:

Word level:

• Which adjectives and adverbs in these extracts help to create a sense of unease and tension?

Sentence level:

• How does the tone of the language used by Nicholas encourage us to listen to him?

Text level:

• How do the stage directions combine with Nicholas speaking to the audience to develop the narrative in the extracts?

The Granny Project

Extract 1

ACT I

The play takes place in a large, untidy family kitchen and living area. On one side, stools surround a table in front of the oven, sink and fridge. On the other, two tatty armchairs and a few floor cushions are grouped around a television. There are several doors off. The table is set for four, with sausages and mashed potatoes already cooling on the plates.

NICHOLAS comes in, eyeing one of the closed doors uneasily. He hushes the audience chatter with a damping down gesture of two spread hands.

NICHOLAS
Sssh. Sssh! You'll have to be quiet, all of you. It's very important. My gran's in there, behind that door, and she needs absolute quiet. She's busy. She's dying. For all I know, she could be dead already. (*He takes a plastic toy soldier off the table and starts twisting its arms and legs around nervously.*) It's been going on for a week now, her dying. Everyone's worn out. Mum and Dad especially. They've been taking turns to sit up with her every night since Monday. Dad's got huge bags under his eyes. Mum looks grey. (*He puts the toy down and faces the audience squarely.*) It's all my brother Ivan's fault. Well Tanya – she's my sister – she says it's all his fault. But Tanya's always saying spiteful things. Sophie – she's my other sister – she tries to shut Tanya up, but … oh this is hopeless. This is no way to explain. I'll have to go right back to the beginning and tell you how it happened from the very start, weeks and weeks ago, the day the doctor first came round to our house to fill in the forms.

HENRY, NATASHA, IVAN, SOPHIE, TANYA and the DOCTOR come in. The children take their places at the table and start eating silently but very fast. HENRY hunches gloomily on one of the chairs. NATASHA leans against a door with a contemptuous look on her face. The DOCTOR sits upright, filling in his long form.

NICHOLAS
(*Taking his place at the table.*) There we all were, minding our own business, politely eating our supper.

IVAN suddenly spins a sausage off his plate onto the floor and reaches down with a fork to stab it … .

Extract 2

ACT III

NICHOLAS comes in, hushing the audience just as he did at the very start of the play.

NICHOLAS
Sssh. Ssssh! There you all go again, making that awful din. Mind you, it is hard to keep quiet the whole time. We know all about that. Since Granny fell ill, we've had to go pussyfooting round the house remembering not to slam doors, and think twice before we even flush a lavatory. She's not getting any better, either. First that collapse, that gave us all so much of a fright! Then, while she was still weak and poorly from that, she caught a terrible cold off Ivan and now they're all shaking their heads and saying "Bronchitis". The doctor's given her penicillin and all that stuff; but apparently things aren't so simple when you're as old as Granny is. It's different if you're young. All they gave Ivan was a box of tissues.

IVAN comes in wearing a dressing gown and clutching a box of tissues. He blows his nose noisily as SOPHIE and TANYA come in another door.

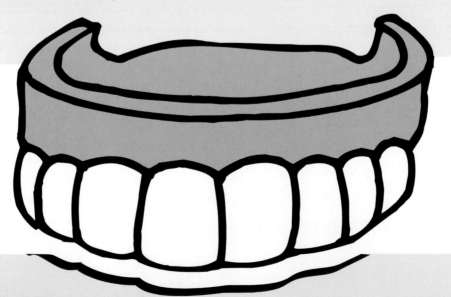

⑥

The director's eye

About the chapter

This chapter looks at the stagecraft issues of script and screenplay writing and focuses on the information the director needs to take into account in order to create the right mood and atmosphere. The three extracts here are from stage and TV, each making their own demands on the director in different ways. In each case, the writer has to use a director's eye when composing the screenplay or script, imagining the text 'living'.

About the text

The first extract in this section is taken from the popular TV sitcom *Absolutely Fabulous*, starring the writer, Jennifer Saunders, and Joanna Lumley. It tracks the life of a 'forty something' mother, Edina, and her friend Patsy, who find it hard to cope with getting older and dealing with everyday life. This extract begins by showing up the role reversal between Edina and her daughter. Edina is behaving like a teenager, trying on lots of clothes in her bedroom, hoping to find the right 'look', whilst her sensible daughter, Saffron, is downstairs in the kitchen with her grandmother.

As you read these extracts, consider the following features of the text:

Word level:

- How does Edina's mother's choice of vocabulary create a sense of comedy in the scene?

Sentence level:

- How does Edina's dialogue add to our understanding of her character (created by the stage directions at the very beginning of the scene)?

Text level:

- How does the scriptwriter convey different emotions through the characters in this extract?

Previous page: a scene from the stage play of *Twelfth Night*.

Absolutely Fabulous 'Poor'

Scene One EDINA'S Bedroom. Day One

EDINA is getting dressed into very 70s gear and make-up. She is plucking her eyebrows, sticking sequins on her face and glitter on her body. For every item she puts on, one is discarded. Jewellery and clothes are thrown around the room. When she is ready, she turns and the whole amazing outfit is revealed.

EDINA [admiring herself in the mirror]
   Hallo, 1992!

Scene Two EDINA'S kitchen. Day One.

SAFFRON is there. MOTHER is also there but at the cooker and not immediately visible. EDINA enters.

EDINA
Sorry I was so long, darling. I had to clear out my wardrobe, get rid of all these horrible, revolting, unfashionable clothes that I simply would not wear, darling, because they are not fashion. I've put them on the floor to throw out.

MOTHER
I thought you'd put them on, dear.

EDINA
What are you doing here?

MOTHER
Oh, I just thought I'd make the most of the house while you can still afford to keep it up.

EDINA
Thank you, and how is it that when I look at you all I see is wear-and-tear, wear-and-tear.

MOTHER [looking at EDINA]
I say, I remember those trousers.

EDINA
No, you don't.

MOTHER
Still hung on to those? Mind you, I'm surprised you can still get into them. It was rather like trying to get toothpaste back into the tube, even then.

EDINA
These are new … . Tell her, Saffy darling. The 70s are back.

MOTHER
Oh! Does that mean you'll be voting Labour again, dear?

EDINA [to SAFFRON]
I've always voted Labour, sweetie. Anyway, I'm only talking about fashion.

SAFFRON

Thank God for that. I wouldn't want to go through that childhood again.

EDINA

Oh, darling – make Mummy a cup of coffee, darling. Would you, sweetie, from the new machine, darling?

MOTHER

Oooh, a chappaccino.

EDINA [spelling it out]

C–A–P–P–U–C–C–I–N–O. All right. [To SAFFRON] Oh, go on, darling. Make the most of Mummy while you're still at home, before you run away to be a student.

SAFFRON goes to coffee machine.

MOTHER [to SAFFRON]

Oh, you told her, dear. Well done.

EDINA

Oh, God! Although why anybody wants to be a student nowadays is a mystery to me, No fun, darling, no demos, no experimental drug-taking. You're just industry-fodder, darling. At least in my day, darling, people used to go to university just to close them down. What will your protest be, darling, a pair of stripy tights and some liquorice allsort earrings? Oh, wow! Call out the National Guard.

MOTHER [to SAFFRON]

Just jealous, dear.

EDINA [reacting]

I could have been a student.

MOTHER

Oh-ho-ho. Thick as two short planks, her reports said.

SAFFRON goes to the fridge.

EDINA

It did not say that, it did not say that. Ask Patsy, darling. She wrote most of them.

SAFFRON

There's no milk.

EDINA

Oh, no milk. Haven't Harrods been here yet, darling? They're normally here by now, aren't they?

SAFFRON

I'll pop out and get some.

EDINA

Oh, no, that would be a complete waste of money.

SAFFRON

And how would you know? When was the last time you bought a carton of milk?

EDINA

A carton? Now stop it. Stop getting all hung up about money, darling. It's pounds and shillings and pence to me.

SAFFRON

It probably was the last time you had anything to do with it. The Queen carries more cash. Your whole life is on account.

EDINA

Oh, stop it. I'll have it black, all right.

MOTHER [to SAFFRON]

I'll have a black chappuccina, Saffy.

EDINA [to MOTHER]

Espresso.

MOTHER

Yes, I am in rather a hurry. As a matter of fact, I think I'd better be off. I want to catch the post.

EDINA

Oh, dear! What a strange archaic little world you live in, isn't it?

SAFFRON

Bye, Gran.

SAFFRON

Bye, dear.

EDINA

Just leave. Oh, and that reminds me, just leave and go straight out that front door. Do not go upstairs to my bedroom and steal things.

MOTHER [to SAFFRON]

I don't know what she's talking about. She's deranged.

EDINA

I passed that sad little excuse for a charity shop yesterday. I saw your little piece of handiwork in the window.

MOTHER looks a little guilty.

EDINA

Must be the only genuine Lacroix, Versace, quilty bedspread in existence.

SAFFRON

Gran!

MOTHER

It was in a bin-liner.

EDINA [to SAFFRON]

It was my dry-cleaning, darling. [to MOTHER] Go on, just get out.

SAFFRON

Bye, Gran.

MOTHER

Goodbye, dear. [to EDINA] Oh, by the way, if you do hit hard times and there is anything you need to sell, my friend Hermione has this little shop.

Hands EDINA the card.

EDINA [reading aloud]

'Bric-a-brac 'n' nic 'n' nacs, things – any old junk taken.' [to MOTHER] Why don't you trade yourself in? Get out, go on, go on.

MOTHER

She'd give you a very good price, dear.

EDINA

Oh, just leave.

MOTHER

I'm only trying to help. Arriva derky.

SAFFRON

Bye, Gran.

MOTHER leaves.

About the text

The following extract is taken from the popular TV series *EastEnders*. In this episode, written by Tony Jordan, Kat is in hospital having attempted to commit suicide after the revelation that her 'sister' Zoe is really her daughter, following a rape when she was a teenager. The reference to the 'man in the moon' refers to (her father) Charlie's promise when she was a child that the man in the moon would always protect her from harm.

The extract produced here is taken from the end of the programme as the characters are trying to come to terms with the events of the day.

As you read this extract, consider the following features of the text:

Word level:

- How does the writer use particular filming abbreviations to establish the impact of the scene on the audience, and as a guide for the director and actors?

Sentence level:

- What effect do the short sentences in Charlie's speech have as he sits by Kat's bedside?

Text level:

- Why do you think the writer chose to include filming directions at the end of the episode without any dialogue?

- Why does he finish with the camera fixed on the moon in the sky?

- How is this a repeating feature of the extract? How is it linked to the characters and their actions towards the end?

Zoe Slater, played by Michelle Ryan, and Kat Slater, played by Jessie Wallace.

EastEnders

SCENE 36/43. ICU FAMILY ROOM.

INT. NIGHT. 03.55.

STUDIO D

> [LYNNE AND LITTLE MO SIT IN SILENCE, SLEEPY.
>
> CHARLIE ENTERS]

LITTLE MO: Dad!

> [LITTLE MO GETS UP AND CUDDLES HIM]

CHARLIE: I know, they told me what happened.

LITTLE MO: It was horrible.

CHARLIE: Have you heard any more?

LYNNE: She's still sleeping, but everything seems alright. Did you see Garry?

CHARLIE: Him and Mark are calling who they can tonight, they'll do the rest in the morning.

LYNNE: Was he really upset?

CHARLIE: Mark's with him.

LYNNE: Poor love.

CHARLIE: Where's Zoe?

LYNNE: We thought she was with you.

CHARLIE: What?

LITTLE MO: She ran off, we thought she'd gone home.

CHARLIE: How long ago?

LYNNE: About quarter past... .

CHARLIE: I must have missed her, I'll go and phone, make sure she's okay... .

[AS CHARLIE IS LEAVING, MO ENTERS;]

Everything alright?

MO: Yeah. I phoned Neville, he came and picked her up.

CHARLIE: She's gone home?

MO: She wanted to come here, but the state she was in... . I said we'd call her.

CHARLIE: Yeah, okay ... [A BEAT] Sit with them eh?

[MO NODS AND JOINS OTHERS, CHARLIE LEAVES]

CUT TO:

SCENE 36/44. SLATERS', ZOE'S

BEDROOM. INT. NIGHT. 03.57.

STAGE 1

[ZOE, CRYING. SHE TAKES HOLDALL FROM WARDROBE, PUTS IT ON BED AND STARTS THROWING CLOTHES IN.

HAVING DONE THIS, SHE SEES TEDDY BEAR ON BED.

SHE PICKS IT UP, A BEAT THEN THROWS IT DOWN AGAIN, PICKING UP HOLDALL AND LEAVING ROOM]

CUT TO:

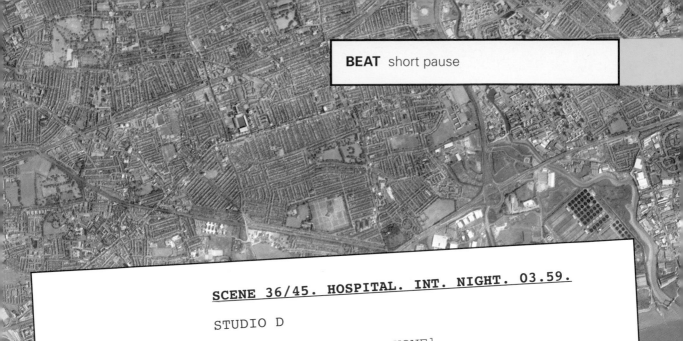

BEAT short pause

SCENE 36/45. HOSPITAL. INT. NIGHT. 03.59.

STUDIO D

    [CHARLIE ON PAYPHONE]

<u>CUT TO:</u>

SCENE 36/46. SLATERS'. INT. NIGHT. 03.59.

STAGE 1

    [ZOE COMES DOWNSTAIRS WITH HOLDALL AS
    TELEPHONE STARTS RINGING.

    SHE IGNORES IT, LOOKS AROUND HOUSE.

    SHE SEES FAMILY PHOTOGRAPH ON WALL.

    LAMENTS THE FAMILY SHE FEELS SHE'S LOST.

    A BEAT, THEN SHE LOOKS AT PHONE.

    MOVES TOWARDS IT]

<u>CUT TO:</u>

<u>**SCENE 36/47. HOSPITAL. INT. NIGHT. 03.59.**</u>

STUDIO D

    [CHARLIE ON PAYPHONE.

    NO ANSWER. HE LETS IT RING.

    LITTLE MO JOINS HIM]

<u>**LITTLE MO:**</u> Dad? They said you can go in and see her.

    [CHARLIE NODS]

D'you want me to come with you?

<u>**CHARLIE:**</u> No, give us a minute on our own eh? Do you mind?

<u>**LITTLE MO:**</u> [SMILES] 'Course not... .

    [A BEAT, CHARLIE LOOKS AT TELEPHONE RECEIVER, RELUCTANTLY PUTS IT DOWN]

                        <u>**CUT TO:**</u>

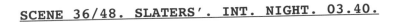

SCENE 36/48. SLATERS'. INT. NIGHT. 03.40.

STAGE 1

    [ZOE REACHES FOR PHONE JUST AS IT STOPS RINGING.

    A BEAT, THEN SHE TURNS TO FRONT DOOR, OPENS IT AND IS GONE;

    OUT ON FAMILY PHOTOGRAPH;]

                                                       CUT TO:

SCENE 36/49. SQUARE. EXT. NIGHT. 04.00.

LOT

    [ZOE CROSSES DESERTED SQUARE.

    SHE PASSES QUEEN VIC – WALKS AWAY DOWN BRIDGE STREET CARRYING HOLDALL.

    SHE ROUNDS CORNER INTO TURPIN ROAD AND IS GONE.]

                                                       CUT TO:

Kat Slater, played by Jessie Wallace, in an earlier scene.

SCENE 36/50. ICU. INT. NIGHT. 04.01.

STUDIO D

> [NURSE LEADS CHARLIE TO KAT'S BED WHICH IS POSITIONED BY LARGE WINDOW]

NURSE: Two minutes.

> [CHARLIE NODS AND NURSE LEAVES HIM.
>
> HE LOOKS DOWN AT KAT. HER WRISTS BANDAGED, STILL ON DRIP, BUT ALL TUBES HAVE GONE FROM HER FACE NOW.
>
> SHE SLEEPS - CHILD-LIKE;
>
> HE SITS ON CHAIR BESIDE HER, HOLDING HER HAND]

CHARLIE: How did it get to this eh? [A BEAT] My little princess. [A BEAT, HE STROKES HER HEAD;] You used to wake up every morning singing... and you made me laugh every day from the minute you woke up to the minute you went to bed. I'd forgotten that... . You reminded me tonight, when you said about the man in the moon. I do remember and I'm sorry I lied to you. I didn't mean to. [A BEAT, BECOMING UPSET;] You're so like your mum you see. I think that's why I took it so badly... . [A BEAT] I know you went to her, I know what she did ... I'm sorry I didn't believe you. None of it was your fault was it? You didn't let me down. It was me who let you down. [A BEAT] And I'm not clever enough to find the right words to tell you how sorry I am about that. [cont]

CHARLIE: [cont] But I know one thing. I'll never let you down again... . Never.

> [CHARLIE AWARE THAT NURSE HAS RETURNED AND STANDS BESIDE HIM.
>
> SHE SMILES AT HIM.

ICU intensive care unit

CHARLIE STANDS, KISSES KAT ON THE FOREHEAD AND WALKS AWAY FOLLOWED BY THE NURSE.

CLOSE ON KAT.

A MOMENT, HER HEAD TURNS TO ONE SIDE THEN SHE OPENS HER EYES SLOWLY.

SHE LOOKS OUT OF THE WINDOW AT THE MOON]

CUT TO:

SCENE 36/51. HOSPITAL. EXT. NIGHT. 04.02.

ON SITE LOCATION

[KAT'S POV.

SHOT OF FULL MOON HANGING IN SKY.

BRIGHT]

CUT TO:

SCENE 36/52. PHIL'S. INT. DAYLIGHT. 04.02.

STUDIO D

[PEGGY SITS ON ARMCHAIR, KNEES DRAWN UP TO HER CHEST, A CHILD AGAIN]

CUT TO:

SCENE 36/53. MARK'S. INT. NIGHT. 04.02.

STAGE 1

[GARRY FAST ASLEEP, SITTING UP, PHONE IN HIS LAP]

CUT TO:

SCENE 36/54. ICU FAMILY ROOM. INT. NIGHT.
04.02.

STUDIO D

    [SLEEPY LYNNE AND LITTLE MO, PAN DOWN TO
    THEIR HANDS.

    ENTWINED, CHILD-LIKE]

CUT TO:

SCENE 36/55. SLATERS', ZOE'S BEDROOM. INT.
NIGHT. 04.02.

STAGE 1

[ZOE'S TEDDY BEAR LAYING ON BED]

CUT TO:

SCENE 36/56. ICU. INT. NIGHT. 04.02.

STUDIO D

    [CU OF KAT.

    A SINGLE INVOLUNTARY TEAR ESCAPES AND
    TRICKLES DOWN HER CHEEK]

CUT TO:

SCENE 36/57. HOSPITAL. EXT. NIGHT. 04.02.

ON SITE LOCATION

    [CU OF MOON.

    HOLD]

FADE OUT

About the text

Twelfth Night by William Shakespeare is a story of love, loss, disguise and humour. This scene deals with one of the main characters, Olivia, the lady of the house and her 'steward' or assistant, Malvolio. The extract continues a sub-plot in which Malvolio is set up to look foolish by other characters who wish to see him get his come-uppance. They have forged a letter from Olivia to him, in which she appears to profess her love for him. In fact, she loves someone else. Malvolio responds to the deliberately humorous requests contained in the letter.

As you read this extract, consider the following features of the text:

Word level:

- Which words act as cues to other characters in the scene?

Sentence level:

- Why do you think Olivia questions Malvolio with just the words 'thy yellow stockings' and 'cross-gartered' instead of using a full sentence? What effect does this have on the scene?

Text level:

- How does the dialogue of the characters suggest behaviour and movement that we would normally expect to find in stage directions?

A scene from a stage performance of *Twelfth Night*.

Twelfth Night

ACT III SCENE IV. OLIVIA's garden.

Enter OLIVIA and MARIA

OLIVIA
(*Aside*) I have sent after him, he says he'll come.
How shall I feast him? What bestow of him?
For youth is bought more oft than begged or
borrowed.
I speak too loud.
(*To MARIA*) Where's Malvolio? He is sad and civil,
And suits well for a servant with my fortunes.
Where is Malvolio?

MARIA
He's coming, madam, but in very strange
manner. He is sure possessed, madam.

OLIVIA
Why, what's the matter? Does he rave?

MARIA
No, madam, he does nothing but smile. Your ladyship were best to have some guard about you if he come, for sure the man is tainted in's wits.

OLIVIA
Go call him hither.

Exit MARIA

I am as mad as he,
If sad and merry madness equal be.

Enter MALVOLIO, cross-gartered and wearing yellow stockings, with MARIA.

How now, Malvolio?

MALVOLIO
Sweet lady, ho, ho!

OLIVIA
Smil'st thou?
I sent for thee upon a sad occasion.

MALVOLIO
Sad, lady! I could be sad. This does make some obstruction in the blood, this cross-gartering, but what of that? If it please the eye of one, it is with me as the very true sonnet is, 'Please one, and please all'.

OLIVIA
Why, how dost thou, man? What is the matter with thee?

MALVOLIO
Not black in my mind, though yellow in my legs. It did come to his hands, and commands shall be executed. I think we do know the sweet roman hand.

OLIVIA
Wilt thou go to bed, Malvolio?

MALVOLIO
(*kissing his hand*) To bed? 'Ay, sweetheart, and I'll come to thee.'

OLIVIA
God comfort thee. Why dost thou smile so, and kiss thy hand so oft?

MARIA
How do you, Malvolio?

MALVOLIO
At your request? – yes, nightingales answer daws.

MARIA
Why appear you with this ridiculous boldness before my lady?

MALVOLIO
'Be not afraid of greatness' – twas well writ.

OLIVIA
What meanest thou by that, Malvolio?

MALVOLIO
'Some are born great' –

OLIVIA
Ha?

MALVOLIO
'Some achieve greatness' –

OLIVIA
What sayest thou?

MALVOLIO
'And some have greatness thrust
upon them.'

OLIVIA
Heaven restore thee.

MALVOLIO
'Remember who commended thy
yellow stockings' –

OLIVIA
'Thy yellow stockings'?

MALVOLIO
'And wished to see thee cross-
gartered.'

OLIVIA
'Cross-gartered'?

MALVOLIO
'Go to, thou art made, if thou
desirest to be so.'

OLIVIA
Am I made?

MALVOLIO
'If not, let me see thee a servant
still.'

OLIVIA
Why, this is very midsummer
madness.

Enter a SERVANT

SERVANT
Madam, the young gentleman of the
Count Orsino's is returned. I could
hardly entreat him back. He attends
your ladyship's pleasure.

OLIVIA
I'll come to him.

Exit SERVANT

Good Maria, let this fellow be
looked to. Where's my cousin Toby?
Let some of my people have a
special care of him, I would not
have him miscarry for the half of my
dowry.

*Exeunt OLIVIA and MARIA,
severally*

MALVOLIO
O ho, do you come near me now?
No worse man than Sir Toby to look
to me. This concurs directly with
the letter, she sends him on purpose,
that I may appear stubborn to him,
for she incites me to that in the
letter. 'Cast thy humble slough,' says
she, 'be opposite with a kinsman,
surly with servants, let thy tongue
tang arguments of state, put thyself
into the trick of singularity', and

consequently sets down the manner how, as a sad face, a reverend carriage, a slow tongue, in the habit of some sir of note, and so forth. I have limed her, but it is Jove's doing, and Jove make me thankful. And when she went away now, 'let this fellow be looked to.' Fellow! – not 'Malvolio', nor after my degree, but 'fellow'. Why, everything adheres together that no dram of a scruple, no scruple of a scruple, no obstacle, no incredulous or unsafe circumstance – what can be said? – nothing that can be can come between me and the full prospect of my hopes. Well, Jove, not I, is the doer of this, and he is to be thanked.

Re-enter MARIA, with SIR TOBY BELCH and FABIAN

SIR TOBY BELCH
Which way is he, in the name of sanctity? If all the devils of hell be drawn in little, and Legion himself possessed him, yet I'll speak to him.

FABIAN
Here he is, here he is. (*To MALVOLIO*) How is't with you, sir? How is't with you, man?

MALVOLIO
Go off, I discard you. Let me enjoy my private. Go off.

MARIA
Lo, how hollow the fiend speaks within him. Did not I tell you? Sir Toby, my lady prays you to have a care of him.

MALVOLIO
Aha, does she so?

SIR TOBY BELCH
Go to, go to. Peace, peace, we must deal gently with him. Let me alone. How do you, Malvolio? How is't with you? What, man, defy the devil. Consider, he's an enemy to mankind.

MALVOLIO
Do you know what you say?

MARIA
La you, an you speak ill of the devil, how he takes it at heart. Pray God he be not bewitched.

FABIAN
Carry his water to th' wise woman.

MARIA
Marry, and it shall be done tomorrow morning, if I live. My lady would not lose him for more than I'll say.

MALVOLIO
How now, mistress?

MARIA
O Lord!

SIR TOBY BELCH
Prithee hold thy peace, this is not the way. Do you not see you move him? Let me alone with him.

FABIAN
No way but gentleness, gently, gently. The fiend is rough, and will not be roughly used.

SIR TOBY BELCH
Why how now, my bawcock? How dost thou, chuck?

MALVOLIO
Sir!

SIR TOBY BELCH
Ay, biddy, come with me. What, man, 'tis not for gravity to play at cherry-pit with Satan, Hang him, foul collier.

MARIA
Get him to say his prayers. Good Sir Toby, get him to pray.

MALVOLIO
My prayers, minx?

MARIA
No, I warrant you, he will not hear of godliness.

MALVOLIO
Go hang yourselves, all. You are idle shallow things, I am not of your element. You shall know more hereafter.

Exit

SIR TOBY BELCH
Is't possible?

FABIAN
If this were played upon a stage, now, I could condemn it as an improbable fiction.

SIR TOBY BELCH
His very genius hath taken the infection of the device, man.

MARIA
Nay, pursue him now, lest the device take air and taint.

FABIAN
Why, we shall make him mad indeed.

MARIA
The house will be the quieter.

SIR TOBY BELCH
Come, we'll have him in a dark room and bound. My niece is already in the belief that he's mad. We may carry it thus for our pleasure and his penance till our very pastime, tired out of breath, prompt us to have mercy on him, at which time we will bring the device to the bar and crown thee for a finder of madmen. But see, but see.

Enter SIR ANDREW with a paper

FABIAN
More matter for a May morning.

SIR ANDREW
Here's the challenge, read it. I warrant there's vinegar and pepper in't.

FABIAN
Is't so saucy?

SIR ANDREW
Ay – is't? I warrant him. Do but read.

SIR TOBY
Give me.

(*Reads*) 'Youth, whatsoever thou art, thou art but a scurvy fellow.'

FABIAN
Good, and valiant.

SIR TOBY
'Wonder not, nor admire not in thy mind why I do call thee so, for I will show thee no reason for't.'

FABIAN
A good note, that keeps you from the blow of the law.

SIR TOBY
'Thou comest to the Lady Olivia, and in my sight she uses thee kindly; but thou liest in thy throat, that is not the matter I challenge thee for.'

FABIAN
Very brief, and to exceeding good sense (*aside*) -less.

SIR TOBY
'I will waylay thee going home, where if it be thy chance to kill me' –

FABIAN
Good.

SIR TOBY
'Thou killest me like a rogue and a villain.'

FABIAN
Still you keep o'th' windy side of the law – good.

SIR TOBY
'Fare thee well, and God have mercy upon one of our souls. He may have mercy upon mine, but my hope is better, and so look to thyself.
Thy friend as thou usest him, and thy sworn enemy,

Andrew Aguecheek.'

If this letter move him not, his legs cannot. I'll give't him.

MARIA
You may have very fit occasion for't. He is now in some commerce with my lady, and will by and by depart.

⑦

Putting it all together

About the chapter

This chapter focuses on the overall impact of one script or screenplay, in terms of development of character, setting, stagecraft and narrative. Rather than look at a number of different texts, it focuses on one that combines all of these features, the film *Shakespeare in Love*, and also involves an interesting mix of historical fact, invention and extracts from other scripts – namely, Shakespeare's own plays.

writing for impact

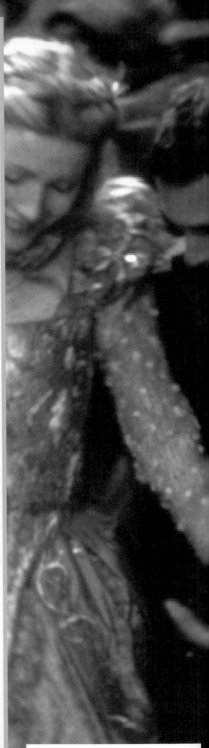

About the text

Shakespeare in Love, directed by John Madden, with a screenplay by Marc Norman and Tom Stoppard, is a fictional representation of part of Shakespeare's life as a playwright in Elizabethan London. However, it is based on a good deal of historical fact about Shakespeare's life and career, and the plays performed in the film are still well known today. In this extract, we see what happens after the ending of a performance of *Romeo and Juliet*, with the part of Juliet having been played by Viola, Will's girlfriend. (In Shakespearean times, women were not allowed to perform on stage and a young man would normally have played the part of a woman.) There are a number of jokes associated with historical events – for example, look at the queen's exit, and the incident with the puddle.

As you read this extract, consider the following features of the text:

Word level:

- Which words and phrases, in both dialogue and stage directions, help us to realise that this is set in a different era?

Sentence level:

- What do you notice about the tone of the queen's dialogue?

Text level:

- How do the stage directions help us form a better picture of the characters in this scene?

- Which aspects of dialogue and stage directions suggest that the character of Will Shakespeare will be financially better off but will lose his girlfriend after this scene?

- Which other texts and events are alluded to in the course of this extract?

This and previous page: a scene from *Shakespeare in Love*, showing Viola, played by Gwyneth Paltrow and Will, played by Joseph Fiennes.

SHAKESPEARE IN LOVE

INT. THE CURTAIN THEATRE. STAGE/AUDITORIUM. DAY.

HIGH ANGLE on audience and stage. 'THE PRINCE' played by WABASH is having the last word.

THE PRINCE
"For never was a story of more woe
Than this of Juliet and her Romeo."

The end. There is complete silence. The ACTORS are worried. But then the audience goes mad with applause.

INT. THE CURTAIN THEATRE. THE INNER CURTAIN/STAGE. DAY.

The inner curtain opens, but WILL and VIOLA, are in a play of their own … embracing and kissing passionately, making their own farewell.

HENSLOWE is too stunned and moved to react at first. Then he looks at the audience and the penny drops. It's a hit.

INT. THE CURTAIN THEATRE. AUDITORIUM/STAGE. DAY.

The audience roars. WILL, VIOLA and THE COMPANY come forward to meet the applause. TILNEY and his MEN burst in. TILNEY jumps up onto the stage, where the ADMIRAL'S MEN are taking their bows. TILNEY'S 'COPS' ring the stage, facing inwards.

TILNEY [shouts triumphantly]
I arrest you in the name of Queen Elizabeth!

The AUDIENCE goes quiet. BURBAGE jumps out of the audience onto the stage.

BURBAGE
Arrest who, Mr Tilney?

TILNEY
Everybody! The Admiral's Men, The Chamberlain's Men and every one of you ne'er-do-wells who stands in contempt of the authority invested in me by her Majesty.

BURBAGE
Contempt? You closed the Rose – I have not opened it.

TILNEY is at a loss but only for a moment.

TILNEY
[he points a 'j'accuse' finger at VIOLA]
That woman is a woman!

The entire audience and the actors recoil and gasp. The NURSE crosses herself.

ALLEYN
What?! A woman?! You mean that goat?!

He points at VIOLA, brazening it out without much chance.

TILNEY
I'll see you all in the clink! In the name of her Majesty Queen Elizabeth –

And an authoritative voice from the audience interrupts him.

VOICE
Mr Tilney …!

It is QUEEN ELIZABETH herself, descending now, her hood and cloak thrown back.

She is an awesome sight. A shaft of sunlight hits her.

QUEEN
Have a care with my name, you will wear it out.

There is a general parting of the waves, soldiers and actors, a general backing off and bowing as QUEEN ELIZABETH takes the limelight.

QUEEN [*CONT'D*]
The Queen of England does not attend exhibitions of public lewdness so something is out of joint. Come here, Master Kent. Let me look at you.

VIOLA comes forward, and is about to curtsey when she catches the QUEEN'S eye, an arresting eye, which arrests the curtsey and turns it into a sweeping bow.

QUEEN [*CONT'D*]
Yes, the illusion is remarkable and your error, Mr Tilney, is easily forgiven, but I know something of a woman in a man's profession, yes, by God, I do know about that. That is enough from you, Master Kent. If only Lord Wessex were here!

VOICE
He is, Ma'am.

The voice belongs to JOHN WEBSTER. He points firmly at a figure in the audience, WESSEX, trying to look inconspicuous.

WESSEX [*weakly*]
Your Majesty … .

QUEEN
There was a wager, I remember … as to whether a play can show the very truth and nature of love. I think you lost it today.

[*turning to WEBSTER*]

You are an eager boy. Did you like the play?

WEBSTER
I liked it when she stabbed herself, your Majesty.

The QUEEN fixes WILL with a beady eye.

QUEEN
Master Shakespeare. Next time you come to Greenwich, come as yourself and we will speak some more.

WILL bows deeply. The QUEEN turns to leave. The waves part for her.

INT. THE CURTAIN THEATRE. MAIN ENTRANCE. DAY.

The QUEEN is bowed out through the doors.

EXT. THE CURTAIN THEATRE. DAY.

A gaggle of the QUEEN'S favoured courtiers wait by her carriage. WESSEX is hurrying down the exterior staircase as the QUEEN emerges from the theatre.
During the following a general egress from the auditorium is taking place, including some of the actors crowding to see her off. WESSEX bows, out of breath.

WESSEX
Your Majesty!

QUEEN
Why, Lord Wessex! Lost your wife so soon?

WESSEX
Indeed I am a bride short. How is this to end?

VIOLA has come out of the theatre, amongst some of the other players. The QUEEN catches her eye.

QUEEN
As stories must when love's denied – with tears and a journey. Those whom God has joined in marriage, not even I can put asunder.

QUEEN [*CONT'D*]
[*she turns to VIOLA*]
Lord Wessex, as I foretold, has lost his wife in the playhouse – go make your farewell and send her out. It's time to settle accounts.

[*to WESSEX*]
How much was the wager?

WESSEX
Fifty shillings.

[*the QUEEN gives him a look*]
Pounds.

QUEEN
Give it to Master Kent. He will see it rightfully home.

[*WESSEX gives his purse to VIOLA.*]

QUEEN [*CONT'D*]
[*to VIOLA*]
And tell Shakespeare something more cheerful next time for Twelfth Night.

The QUEEN proceeds towards her carriage. There is an enormous puddle between her and her carriage. The QUEEN hesitates for a fraction and then marches through the puddle as cloaks descend upon it.

QUEEN [*CONT'D*]
Too late, too late.

She splashes her way into her carriage, which departs.